D1595061

Telling Secrets

An Artist's Journey Through Childhood Trauma

Jane Orleman

CWLA Press • Washington, DC

CWLA Press is an imprint of the Child Welfare League of America. The Child Welfare League of America (CWLA) is a privately supported, nonprofit, membership-based organization committed to preserving, protecting, and promoting the well-being of all children and their families. Believing that children are our most valuable resource, CWLA, through its membership, advocates for high standards, sound public policies, and quality services for children in need and their families.

CHILD WELFARE LEAGUE OF AMERICA, INC.
440 First Street, NW, Third Floor, Washington, DC 20001–2085
E-mail: books@cwla.org

CURRENT PRINTING (last digit)
10 9 8 7 6 5 4 3 2 1

Cover and text design by Jennifer R. Geanakos
Photo credits: page iii, Jackie Bangs;
all other photos, Debbie Storlie-Young

Printed in the United States of America

ISBN # 0–87868–729–7

Library of Congress Cataloging-in-Publication Data

Orleman, Jane.
    Telling secrets : an artist's journey through childhood trauma /
Jane Orleman.
        p. cm.
    Includes bibliographical references.
    ISBN 0–87868–729–7
    1. Adult child sexual abuse victims. 2. Art therapy.
3. Psychoanalysis. I. Title.
RC489.A7074 1998   97–51413
616.85′8369--dc21

**Dedicated to my life's companion,
Richard Elliott.**

Dick & Jane—Spring 1997

Acknowledgments

My special thanks to Andrew D. Whitmont, Ph.D., who is the Dr. W. referred to in the text.

I also wish to honor the following:

Greg Green, who made me aware of my need to make art, and his mother, Eveleth Green, director of the first gallery to exhibit these images.

The many curators, publishers, and reporters who, by their support, continued to spread the seed.

The open–hearted people who viewed the exhibits and shared their lives with me.

The Ucross Foundation and Art Matters, Inc., for time and funds to work.

Susan Brite and the Child Welfare League of America for the vision and courage to publish this material.

Linda Cole, who patiently and diligently transcribed my dreams and reflections.

My husband, Dick Elliott, for encouragement, insights, and enthusiasm.

Portions of this book have previously appeared in the following:

Calyx: A Journal of Art & Literature by Women

Claman, E. (Ed.). (1994). *Each in her own way*. Eugene, OR: Queen of Swords Press.

Claman, E. (Ed.). (1995). *Writing our way out of the dark: An anthology by child abuse survivors*. Eugene, OR: Queen of Swords Press.

Courtois, C. A. (1993). *Adult survivors of child sexual abuse*. Milwaukee, WI: Families International.

Hurricane Alice

Journal of Child Sexual Abuse

Journey

Journal of the American Art Therapy Association

Northwest Review

Sojourner

The Sun: A Magazine of Ideas

Treating Abuse Today

Contents

List of Illustrations

Foreword

Therapists have long known that the affects from childhood trauma can extend into adulthood. Natural biological survival responses emerge within children when they are traumatized. These responses often create disturbing conditions that do not disappear. A profound example is the loss of the trauma survivor's voice—the inability to identify and speak about personal physical or emotional pain. Exacerbating this problem is the fact that adults abused as children may have had caregivers who were unable to support their healing. This leads a child to feel unimportant, even invisible. Consequently, those who experienced abuse or other trauma can have difficulty standing up for themselves, modulating their anger, and giving meaning to their own experiences.

Another "condition" in those who were terrorized in childhood is the habit of "intellectualizing" their past trauma. This is a common defense acquired as a result of anxiety caused by reminders or triggers related to their terror–evoking event. Engaging in discussion or otherwise direct confrontation about their experience can create overwhelming anxiety. Being overly intellectual and logical compensates for the fear of being enveloped by harsh feelings.

The beginning task for those who are faced with reconciling their traumatic experiences is to unlock their defensive conditions, or "gatekeepers," in order to bring about healing. Indigenous communities know how to do this through their carefully prescribed rituals. These rituals use dancing, drumming, chanting, and artwork effectively to reach a troubled person. They also provide a safe way for trauma survivors to break through their defenses. Just as our animal friends cautiously peek out from their burrows, human beings must experience physical and psychological safety before addressing their fears. Moving beyond gatekeepers allows the healing to begin. The traumatic experience can then be transformed into renewed quality of life.

Wisely, doing what indigenous peoples have known to do, Jane Orleman has used art to dissolve her gatekeepers. Speaking through her paintings, Jane tells her poignant story of rediscovering her "voice" and, ultimately, healing her pain. Now, through this book, she gives her suffering meaning by sharing herself and her work with readers who may be struggling with their own recovery.

Every one of us is special in having the capability to overcome our defenses in order to transform our lives. We may use music, song, writing—there are thousands of ways. Let Jane's journey to healing give you the courage to express yourself, so that your presence is known in the world.

Kathryn Brohl, M.A., L.M.F.T.
Licensed Marriage and Family Therapist
Author: Working with Traumatized Children: A Handbook for Healing
When Your Child Has Been Molested: A Parent's Guide
Pockets of Craziness: Investigating Suspected Incest

Introduction:
My Life as an Artist

Art has long been an effective and valuable means of exploring and communicating social and spiritual crisis. It was not until the 20th century, however, that the visual arts began to examine the crises of a woman's soul.

The paintings included here speak of violation: emotional, physical, and sexual, specifically within the home. They depict the experiences and their effects in later life. These effects are so hidden that many of us who have been actively entangled seem to be unaware of them. The viewpoint is that of the female child and the woman she later becomes. The grief, despair, and pain inflicted on the souls of the victims, survivors, perpetrators, and the family members, however, affect us all. The crippling results are handed down from adult to child for generations.

The masculine and feminine aspects of humanity have been out of balance for eons, resulting in crimes against the soul. The first step in stopping the violation of ourselves and our children is to acknowledge those violations. With that in mind, I offer you my story.

My Story

In searching my memory for the first time I had an impulse to speak visually, I find myself 8 years of age on a hot summer day, walking to the local swimming hole, Silver Lake. We lived on a farm at the time, so my path was down the cow lanes to the quiet pool. I was alone that day and at peace, so I could notice the world around me. I was awestruck by the beauty of the still pool filled with water lilies in full bloom. Light filtered through surrounding trees, dancing on the water in company with the dragon flies. There was a hum of insect and bird songs. I was rooted to the spot for so long that a turtle crossed the road at my feet. I retraced my steps back home in a dreamlike state to collect paper and crayons. I returned to the pool that day and for many days afterwards in an attempt to capture the beauty and the magic of that time and place. It would be more accurate, however, to say that *I* was captured. The more I drew, the deeper I was drawn into the wondrous nature of nature.

It was a transforming experience, but it was not the art maker in me that was awakened; it was the earth lover. For the next 10 years, I walked the wooded hills near my home, finding comfort in their silent beauty. This experience provided the grounding to see me through years of pain, violation, and confusion.

Recently an interviewer, who was trying to discover the seed of my interest in art, asked what I had collected as a child. I surprised us both when I answered, "Trees."

Memories of favorite trees came back to me: safe trees, trees that I climbed to spend time in and with, listening to the breeze, the birds, and the quiet. The clouds and the stars above were more of my world than the people below. I used to enjoy making treasure maps showing the way to my many hiding places in trees around the town.

I was a solitary child but felt truly alone only when I was with people. A child who has deep and shameful secrets becomes isolated by the need to keep those secrets. I was fortunate to have a brother who was and continues to be a friend. We were certainly not perfect angels as children, but there has always been love, support, and protection between us. It was important back then to have a witness who could assure me that I was sane; that it was our world that was crazy. Most of the memories recorded in this book are of events that I have pushed deep into the recesses of my mind but have never forgotten. These are not memories recovered through hypnosis, but even so it is reassuring that I do have a witness to those years. While that brother's memories are different than mine, from another point of view, the pieces fit the same puzzle. Another sibling seems to have grown up in a parallel universe, with memories so different from ours that they include a father who was a loving disciplinarian. Ten people in a house together may have ten quite different memories of events in that house, and they will all contain the truth. I can only share the world as I experienced it.

There were many levels to the secrets, but one that permeated our lives was that Dad was a violent alcoholic. He made our lives a misery and, between rages, bought us presents to atone. It would be easy to lay the blame for all of our shared pain at his door. But I find myself wondering about his childhood. His parents divorced when he was five. He was raised by his mother, grand-mother, and great-grandmother. Though his father lived in the same town, he didn't see him for a decade. During his teenage years, he was called upon to fix the needles for his mother, who was addicted to morphine. On his paternal side, there were generations of raging alcoholics.

I am inclined to say there are no easy answers, no end to the trail of blame. My mother also came from a broken home. Together, they did their best, handicapped as they were by their own childhood experiences. I thought we were different because of the violent chaos in our home. I know now that the secret lives of many of our neighbors were much the same.

My earliest memories are of being molested. Between the ages of 3 and 8, it happened often. Between the ages of 9 and 13, I was subject to almost daily emotional, physical, or sexual assault. Rarely did a day go by without violence.

I passed my teenage years in a daze of prescription drugs and alcohol. Until recently, I had adopted the attitude that this had all happened in a long-dead past. Now I realize that, by declaring the past dead, I was cut off from my source. I was living in a house with no foundation. Painting the images in this book has helped me to accept the events that shaped my view of myself and the world for the past 40 years.

I was 20 when I eloped with my first husband. It was difficult to leave home, as it meant leaving my 7-year-old brother. He had been the light of my life since I was 13. During the next six years, I traveled the country with John while he completed his education. It was a peaceful time for us. I think we had both married to get away from home. I had been attracted to him partly because he was a craftsman. His creativity fulfilled a need in me. The marriage failed, because I needed to find my own creative center rather than live through him.

By the time I was 26 years old, I had been drifting in and out of college for nine years. I had attended five different universities, constantly changing majors, while yearning for meaningful occupation. When I arrived at Central Washington University as a senior, I intended to study geography, a reasonable choice for someone seeking direction. I still loved to draw maps.

Discovering Art

Soon after arriving at the university, a newfound friend took me through the art department. He said, "You can make art. You *need* to make art." I began with stick figures. Knowing that I had found my life's work, I changed majors for the last time and enjoyed three exciting years completing a B.A. in art. My art work in college was full of sexual imagery mixed with humor and spirituality.

In the eight years after leaving the university, I painted interiors in an effort to learn my craft by rendering the world around me. I spent hundreds of hours painting my home with flowers on the table, the dog in a chair, everything in its place. There was never any overturned furniture, no signs of a struggle. For many years, there were no people. Gradually, my new husband and I came into the picture. As soon as people arrived, so did sexual content.

During the next eight years I returned to the major inspiration from my college days, a need to express my sexuality in spiritual terms. The style of this work has become my symbolic or "archetypal" voice. Images that center me and speak of completeness are painted in this style. In retrospect, I see that both of these directions set the stage for my current work. The interiors created the foundation for my recent work in my "child's" voice. They also provided grounding or a sense of safety, which I desperately needed.

Searching for Help

I had been playing hide and seek with my past for a long time, using drugs, alcohol, and distance to protect me. Since I had put a 3,000-mile buffer between me and my parents for 15 years, I was totally unprepared when they came for a visit and then decided to stay. Within three days they had bought a house. Thus began five years of desperately trying to please them and hating myself for doing it. For three of those years I paid weekly visits to a therapist in an effort to cope with my out-of-control emotions.

That early attempt at therapy coincided with a change in my painting style and imagery, from the interiors to the symbolic. I was unconsciously taking my sexual conflict and projecting it to a cosmic setting millions of miles away. The paintings from this period were filled with stars. The moon became a reoccurring symbol of the protecting and destroying elements in the nature of the feminine. Working with the sexual material in this way allowed me to create a safe distance from which to relate to the horrifying experiences of my early life.

Then I began to experience a creative block. For the next few years I painted portraits just to keep my skills alive and growing. But I knew there was a creative crisis brewing. I found it increasingly difficult to enter my studio. Three years earlier, my parents had finally left the state, motivated by my insistence that I could not live with them in my daily life. I knew that I might be overwhelmed by guilt for having driven my parents away, but by being aware and vigilant, I was able to keep guilt at bay for several years. I accomplished this at a great price: shutting down my thoughts and emotions to the point of becoming a vacuum. I was spending my time playing endless games of solitaire, reading science fiction, and smoking cigarettes.

I think now that the art I *needed* to do was art that I was not yet *ready* to do. I had to become desperate before I would be willing to paint the images living inside me. Then something happened that brought the inner crisis to my conscious attention. My mother died in an accident while on her way to visit me. My mother appeared to disapprove of my artwork, and when she came to visit I agonized over which paintings to hide away. Perhaps my perception of her disapproval was a projection of my own self-condemnation, but whatever the case, I am sure I couldn't have painted these images from my childhood if she was here to see them.

With her death, the awareness of my own mortality caught my attention. Life is short. I needed to use my time here to do my work, to enjoy my life, my garden, my home, my body; to share the fullness of all my experiences with my husband. But, in fact, I had shut out the world in an attempt to keep painful emotions from overwhelming me. I was so successful that I didn't know *why* I had narrowed my life to two chairs, a deck of cards, a stack of books and my smokes.

Smoking was making me sick. If I continued, life would be short and miserable. I had tried to quit many times in the past 35 years, but it was the only socially acceptable form of suicide left to me, a way to express my self-hatred. Now it was time to make a choice for life. This choice led me to a psychologist who occasionally used hypnosis to help a smoker quit the habit, but more often, I think, he turned away that work as a poor use of his time. His stop-smoking program was a seven-hour package deal. In the first two-hour session, I quit. There I was with five paid-up hours of therapy. So I said, "Maybe you can help me with this other little problem—a creative block." I had hoped for the same kind of magic: quit smoking, start painting. It wasn't that easy. In fact, hypnosis was seldom used during the years we worked together. When he did use hypnosis, it was usually to help create a sense of safety.

It seemed by chance that I met Dr. W., a Ph.D. in clinical psychology. He was the third psychologist I had gone to in my quest to quit smoking. Had one of the other attempts been successful, my life would have unfolded differently. Whether chance or destiny brought us together, mutual trust and respect enabled us to work together for seven years. His techniques were varied, but the most dramatic experience came in an early session when Dr. W. introduced a breathing exercise similar to the type of breathing used in childbirth. I don't know what his expectations were, but it provoked a tremendously deep response from within me. I cried out in pain, sobbed, and felt great fear. This was incredible to me, as I am usually quite self-contained. He assured me that I could stop this experience at any moment. I realized, however, that if my response was this powerful, it was too important to leave unfinished. He asked me what past experience these feelings evoked. I said, "The Rape."

"How old are you?"
"11."
"Who is there?"
I named the five older boys who were there.

Through the intensity of this experience I realized that the past still held me imprisoned. My fear had frozen my feelings. I have never forgotten the events. Over the years, I had even spoken of the rape to other therapists and my husband. But my emotions had been kept well-hidden. They had been stored safely away. Now, like Pandora, I had opened the box.

In the following week, I wrote down many of my painful secrets, a childhood biography. I took the pages to the next therapy session. Handing them to Dr. W., I said, "There, now you know what happened. I don't want to talk about it."

Later, in going through a box of stuff, I came across a similar document that I had written for a therapist 10 years earlier. I was amazed to discover this writing, as I had totally forgotten having done it. There was little difference between the two accounts. In both, I mention the first time I used art to tell my secrets. I was in fifth grade when I drew a picture of my teacher "doing it." The drawing was intercepted as I passed it to another student. The power of art to communicate was certainly demonstrated that day.

Painting My Story

I was two months into the therapy process and had done only one or two unfinished paintings. Dr. W. dropped a stone into these still waters. He asked, "Have you ever painted from your own life experiences?" I resisted the idea at first, and he said, "What else do you *have*?" The logic of it struck me! Of course; this is the life I have been given. To ignore it as a creative source would be tantamount to denying my own existence.

So I began this visual dialogue between me and myself, my present and my past, me and my therapist. Once I accepted this journey, I gave myself a set of guidelines. Never censor the creative process. Trust the expressions of my thoughts and feelings as they appear in the paintings. Always share the paintings and be honest with Dr. W. Do the work necessary to face my demons and follow where the path leads me. I started with one or two paintings a month. Their images were inspired by subjects discussed in therapy sessions.

My Child's Voice

Having painted a distant reality for so many years, I found it very difficult to express real events and feelings. After nine months of working with Dr. W., he proposed that I devote an afternoon to thinking, feeling, or acting like a child. That suggestion led to a series of small paintings from the point of view of myself as a child. These images in the child's voice allowed me to say in paint what I found so difficult to say in words. I have been a skeptic about the inner child, but by allowing the child a voice the dam exploded and the creative block was broken. Soon I was doing six to eight paintings a month instead of one or two. About one-third of these were in the child's voice. The rest speak in the symbolic voice and express my reflections as an adult about the painful events in my past and about the process of revealing and accepting those events.

My Emotional Voice

As I progressed, a third painting voice appeared, one that expressed strong emotion. I attribute the development of this "emotional voice" to Dr. W.'s sustained efforts to introduce me to my inner masculine. It was a concept that I resisted vigorously. Visualizing the creative feminine as a well full of water and the creative masculine as the force that draws the water from the well helped me to accept the importance of the inner masculine. I believe now that the acceptance of that masculine energy opened the way for the consuming flow of creativity that followed.

The first of the images from the emotional voice was a result of Dr. W.'s suggestion that I spend an afternoon in a masculine experience mode. I decided to paint like a man, which I whimsically envisioned as big and sloppy. I allowed myself to be crude and cavalier, which unmasked my fears of the masculine energy. It took another nine months of psychotherapy before this first connection with the inner masculine grew into my emotional voice. It meant going beyond crude and cavalier to bold, decisive, potent, and courageous. Rendering images while stimulated by this new and highly charged emotional center was by no means easy.

Safety

One of the things that made this work possible are the "safety paintings." Some are mandalas that create a sheltered place within, others are pictures of safe retreats. Invariably, a safety painting is a harbinger of an image of a deeper revelation charged with heavy emotional impact. In a sense, these paintings are like diving boards to the unconscious. Also, some of these images deal with the process of therapy and the therapeutic relationship. There are a number of obstacles to the process and relationship. We are taught that it's not acceptable to talk about ourselves, to dominate a conversation, or to tell our secrets. In therapy, we do all of these. But once I realized that the past was still alive, I knew that I would need the help of someone who understood emotional and psychic reality as well as physical reality.

My Painting Techniques

I seldom set out to paint a particular event. The image comes to me as I paint. Often I approach the canvas with thoughts brought up in the therapeutic process. For instance, I might sit for a few minutes before I begin and ask myself, "Why is it so hard for me to express anger?" That question resulted in the painting titled *Daddy Enraged*. The painting process results from my deeper self telling me what I feel, think, or, sometimes, remember. Often these are feelings and thoughts of which I am not consciously aware. Openness to this inner dialogue has created the visual evidence detailing a journey of self-discovery.

For example, in a recent image of the gang rape, *Don't Touch Me! I'm Alive*, I am alive, conscious, and protesting. While painting this image, I allowed the terror to wash through me so that it could live on the canvas. Since trying to forget my childhood traumas hadn't worked, I decided to remember them and to interact with those memories. I thought perhaps the acceptance of that reality could rechannel the power it held over my life. That thought bore fruit. In the seven years that my emotional center and life experiences have been the creative source for my artwork, I have painted more than I had in the previous 20 years.

I paint with oils, using a fast-drying medium that I discovered when I began this body of work. The first decision I make about a painting is the size. Sometimes I know immediately which canvas to use, other times I might handle a half a dozen before one feels correct. The child voice is usually a small one, a visual whisper; the emotional voice can be quite large, a shout. However, the reverse has also been true. It has been important to me to keep open to surprise, to not become the director but let the images flow.

At first, I applied the paint with small sable brushes. Once the "emotional voice" became more active, I had a dream that led me into using large palette knives. Soon after that, at Dr. W.'s suggestion, I took up a butcher knife as my primary painting instrument. When I returned to brushes, it was the bold, oversized variety that drew my interest. Now I am apt to use all of these tools on a single painting. I find that I have options in my art and in my life that I didn't have before I began this work.

My Three Voices

The three painting voices—the symbolic, the child, and the emotional—also appear throughout the work as aspects of myself; the hidden self, the child self, and the angry self, all protected by the persona who acts in the world. In 1990, these aspects exhibited degrees of separation, hostility, and unawareness of one another. By 1993, they had an inner and outer awareness that allowed them to name themselves and stand united. I speak of them as characters in an inner drama, but they also have an outer reality as they interact, through me, with the world.

In the process of blending these and other attributes, I have been able to create the paintings, aggressively seek exhibitions, and speak publicly about the work. Looking through the images, I see these and many other aspects of myself that have helped revitalize my view of the world. I do not view these characters as evidence of multiple personalities, but as a means of symbolic self-portrayal. They give me a frame of reference that allows me to expand who I am.

These characters are by no means clearly defined. They weave into one another and evolve through time. There are strong connections between my angry self, the masculine force, and the beast within. Many of the masculine models available to me as a child had been raging, unpredictable, and cruel. Not surprisingly, I depict the masculine force as a wild beast who later became an inner monster, my homicidal maniac. Once he was revealed within me through the paintings, I set out to embrace that part of myself, which I had previously feared and rejected. The monster, who later became androgynous, is still there, and my relationship to it continues to change.

I see the same shifting nature with other symbols that I use, such as the skeleton figure. Early in my work the skeleton represents the perpetrator of overwhelming sexual assault; later it becomes the connection to the lost soul. Both the monster and the skeleton, which initially symbolized my deepest fears, eventually evolved to embody hidden strengths. They also came to hold both masculine and feminine power. Since symbols are alive and ever-changing, they speak across time and space. The same symbol may open a different door for you than it did for me, or a different door for me yesterday than it will tomorrow. Although I suggest meanings for symbols, it must be remembered that they are by nature untranslatable. The symbolic image is a starting point for the contemplation of the complexity of reality.

Dreaming My Story

In an effort to understand the paintings on a conscious level, I began writing a few notes about each one. I soon realized that my dreams amplified the meaning in the paintings and vice versa. In fact, at the same time that I discovered art, 27 years ago, I began a dream journal.

The number of dreams that I have recorded parallels the number of paintings—more than 300 in the last seven years. In the first year, many of the dreams were nightmares, powerful and disturbing. By writing them down and searching for their message with the help of Dr. W., I was able to overcome my fear of these communications from my dream self, a guiding force in the therapy process. Once I showed a willingness to listen, my subconscious awareness had a great deal to say to me.

The dreams associated with the images in this book are usually from the night before or after starting a new painting. The interconnections of the dreams and images are not always readily apparent to me. It is the process of viewing the art and dreams in retrospect that has yielded glimmers of enlightenment. Dr. W. sometimes worked with the dreams in our sessions; however, I have not included dream interpretations per se in this book. Rather, I simply mention connections that I see with the paintings or my process of growth. I try to think of all of the characters in a dream as aspects of myself. So when my husband, Dick, appears in a dream, he represents an inner masculine, usually one who is my friend or guide. I see dreams as parables told to us by the personal and/ or collective unconscious. As such, others can find their own meanings in my dreams just as they might in a story or a poem.

Sharing My Story

As I exhibit, give slide shows, and write about my work, I gain a fuller understanding of its meaning. Often it is the viewer who reflects back to me deeper insights on a particular image. I have been amazed and moved by the responses to the exhibits, which have been used by communities and on university campuses to create an awareness of the emotional wound that devastates our society.

The first time I exhibited paintings depicting sexual and physical violence toward children, I fully expected someone to want my work removed from the gallery. I showed the work to the city lawyer ahead of time. She spoke to the American Civil Liberties Union so that she would be prepared. To our surprise, however, there were no complaints about the exhibit. Survivors, therapists, therapy groups, judges, lawyers, law enforcement people, sex offenders, teachers, high school and college students, those who assist rape victims as well as the general public, came from all over the state to see it. I am grateful that my work has become a tool for learning.

The chapters in this book reflect shifts in emphasis that I realized happened at about one-year intervals. The paintings and dreams appear as they came to me; the most difficult, which represent my first year of therapy, appear in the first chapter, "Awakening." These paintings are intensely personal.

Unfortunately, however, my experiences are not unique. Child molestation and rape are not uncommon; physical violence toward children is a daily occurrence around the globe. Those are obvious traumas, but, as I have learned from the viewers at my exhibits, they are the tip of the iceberg. Divorce, alcoholism, chronic illness, losses due to accidents, or street violence are among the many sources of trauma, guilt, shame, and secrets. In recent years, art exhibits, plays, movies, and books have begun to express this reality. The resulting discussions help to free others to face their secrets. Our secrets can become monsters that consume energy to keep the truth hidden from ourselves and the world long after the original insult is past. Eventually, the monster within does gnaw its way out. It may take 30 or 40 years to free itself, bursting upon the world in a fit of murderous madness or an incredible flood of creativity. Truth-telling does not get rid of the beast, but it does begin to change our relationship with the monster and its effect on us all.

My art, like therapy, explores connections through time and inner space. It speaks of aspects of my self interacting through time—adult to child, child to adult. It depicts the ability to join hands with your true self and interact with your past in a way that affects your future. Past events, feelings, and intentions may become transformed, creating new possibilities. The work in this book expresses the search through the layers within. The process of painting brings these excavations to the surface. The exhibition and publication of the images sets them free, allowing them to travel from my sphere to yours, going from the personal to the collective. I offer you my images, my dreams, and my reflections.

1. Awakening

Dream: First, I was a wandering fisherwoman who painted animals and birds. Later I was in a crowded underground room. We were all milling around. I felt an urgency to get out of there. Finally, I found the door but as I was leaving, the door closed and I was caught in it. I finally got loose and out the door only to find myself in another, less crowded, outer room. We were grabbed and forced against the wall to be searched. I tried to hide my secret message in the moulding around the top of the room. I think it was the key to escape. They found it and I was punished.

A Memory of What We Agreed to Forget

After three months of weekly therapy and little progress, my therapist, Dr. W., and I found the source of my creative block. In this session, I laid on the floor breathing deeply, much like a birthing mother. I found this strangely upsetting and began to sob. Dr. W. pressed on my upper chest with his fingertips and I cried out with pain. Long-suppressed emotions poured out, emotions related to a rape when I was 11 years old.

The area of my chest where he pressed became the apple tree in this image. The many pressure points are represented by the apples, each releasing a bit of emotion stored from past traumas. The mermaid, a creature of the unconscious, offers the apple as mother's milk, a wellspring of health. That the pain is depicted by apples implies there is wisdom to be gained. The fledgling is beginning her quest to become aware. The meditating figure in the womb is myself as I have been during the past 10 years. I have been making paintings full of moons and stars, images of enlightenment in some distant universe. During the same time, I have retreated more and more into myself.

As the dream begins, I am one with the creator. Later, after much difficulty, I am born only to find myself in another crowded room, my body. I am left here until I discover the secret. I believe that when we are born the spirit which animates us is a piece of the Infinite Being. In order to experience our individuality we all agree to forget that we are of the same spirit. We forget that memory of enlightenment. Throughout life we continue to forget. We forget things because they are trivial, incorrect, no longer useful, emotionally painful, traumatic, even because they are dangerous to know. The memory may truly be gone or it may be hidden in the moulding of the mind so that a friendship or family life can continue. The memories become secrets. The secrets that I share with you in this book were locked away in a room in my mind. I have always known where the room was and have had the key to the trunk. I have known most of the contents but have felt safer to leave it unexamined.

Guilt

Dream: *I was living with two women and their older brother, my distant cousins. The brother had been away in the service, but we had all lived together as children. When we were young, the brother had raped me. I was afraid of him and dreaded seeing him. I noticed that someone had hidden a tape recorder under the blankets on my bed. He came into my room with the intention of raping me again. As he talked to me and I answered, I realized that on the tape, it would sound like I was agreeable when really I was just defeated. The next morning at the kitchen table, the two sisters were praising their brother and saying how glad they were to have him home. I got very angry and said "Your brother rrr . . ." All of a sudden my throat closed up, and I couldn't breathe. I fell off my chair clutching my throat. I knew if I said it I would die. I resolved in my mind not to say it and was able to begin breathing again.*

Dr. W. suggested a revolutionary idea—to paint from my own life experience. The idea of painting my life was repellent and frightening to me, but all of the other wells were dry, so I decided to try it. We had talked about my guilt feelings that were associated with being raped, and this became the first image in a narrative of my early life. The secrets that I have kept until now are like bottled poison. The skull and crossbones mark the spot where all of the painful emotions have been stored.

When I was a teenager I had years of tonsillitis, strep throat, bronchitis, and other chest ailments. It was the place in my body where I stored my guilt. I thought I would die if I spoke of it but the silence kept me painfully ill.

Shame

This image reminds me of a mummy—an appropriate analogy, since, as a child, so intense was my shame and self-loathing that I often wished myself dead. The weight of that shame drove me inward and I became a solitary person. Now it is time to unwrap those self-protecting layers to allow old wounds to heal and new skin to grow.

Shame does retreat from all offers of assistance or caring. To release the shame, I fear, one must also explore its source, acknowledge its power, and experience its energy. No wonder my inner patient is afraid.

Dream: *I was a healer. The person who was injured was in great pain but would not allow me to enter his body to heal him. If I didn't heal him, we would both die. He was adamantly against it.*

Beyond the Valley of Shadow

Dream: I was caring for a sick baby, who was not expected to live. I fed it and was pleased that it took the food. Then it burped it up all over my dress. While I was cleaning up myself and the baby, it messed all over my lap, but somehow the baby got better. I took it everywhere with me—in fact, I think it was chained to my waist, as we lived in a dangerous area. The parents were happy with how well their child was doing. I think it had even started to talk.

By the age of 9, I was suicidal. One day while contemplating ways to end my life, I was suddenly comforted by the realization that if I could only survive for another nine years, I would have control of my own life. I told myself to hang on. In this painting, I go back to comfort my younger self, to tell her she can survive. Later she will come to a world of her own making. She will live in a house full of love and flowers.

As Dr. W. and I worked with this dream, he suggested that I actually go back in my mind and comfort the child I was then. Perhaps the comfort I had received in that dark hour of my childhood had indeed come back through the years from me. It seemed a strange idea but worth trying. This was the first time we discussed the Hopi Indian concept of the long body. Think of all you were, are, or will be, as existing at once and contained as part of your body. Within this model you can interact with yourself through time.

Smiling on the Outside

Feelings of rejection have been a major force in my life, so I decided to paint the feeling of being under a cloud with nothing to protect myself. Then I immediately drew the "real" me, a smiling persona, to shield her or, perhaps, to deny her existence as I walk away with my mysterious balloons. Do they contain other, as yet unacknowledged, aspects of my self?

If the ramshackle place in this dream houses my soul, I think it is time to examine the materials going into the grim remodeling project. All of these ground–up memories will continue to be a part of me, but I can expand into new possibilities. I am ready to search for what lies between walls of rejection and a false facade. It frightens me to realize that swimming through the foreboding slime pit is the only way out of here.

Dream: *There was a ramshackle house; maybe we were living in it. We were fixing it up by putting old stuff into a grinder and pouring the chips in a mold. We were making various-sized bricks of this stuff. We used the bricks to build new walls inside the old house—rebuilding the house from the inside out. The view out the back door was a deep pit filled with water ... like a gravel pit but kind of junky. A dangerous place.*

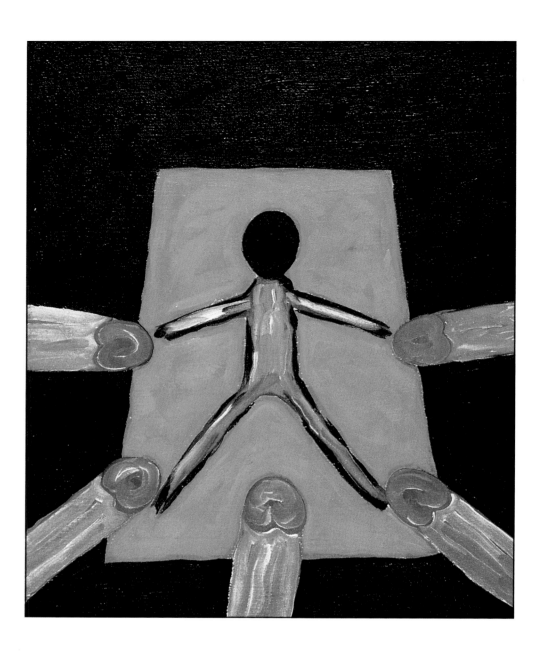

Rape

Dream: *I had dropped a packet of buttons and was reaching down behind a chair to pick them up. Some men came in the room behind me and said, "What do we have here?" I was a young woman in a sundress. They came up behind me, grabbed me, and took off my dress. They laid me down on the coffee table, so that all the men coming to their party could take their turn raping me. I turned myself off and went away in my head.*

I left my therapy session with the words *magnetism* and *potency* to consider. I found these words upsetting without knowing why. I sat crying in front of my easel for an hour or two a day for the next five days. Then, in an hour, I painted this image. I recalled feeling like a magnet that attracted nasty men and boys. As for potency, I felt powerless to defend myself. Of all of the paintings I was to do during this process, *Rape* was, by far, the most difficult. I shared a photo of it with Dr. W., but I hid it from my husband for five months. I had allowed that event back into my consciousness along with the terror and shame. The impact was enormous.

The resonance between the painting and dream wraps me in pulsating blackness. I know that I am the one who has to bring myself back to the light.

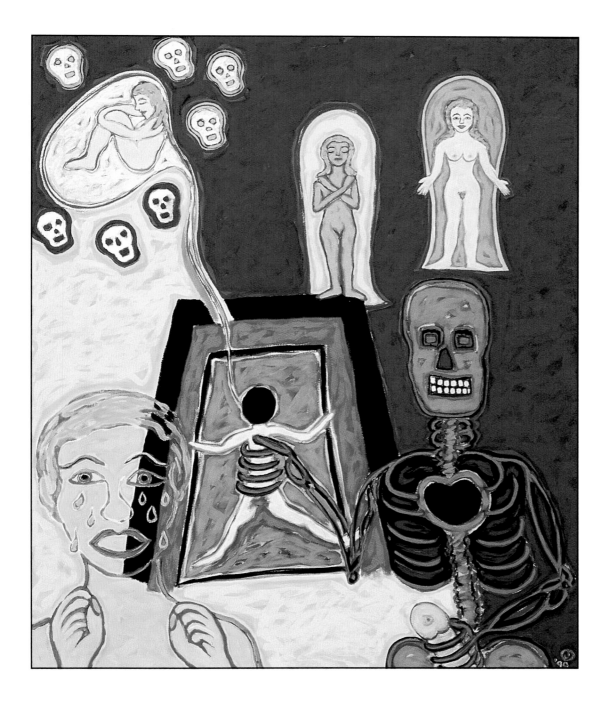

In the Grip of the Fate Worse Than Death

The child has "gone off." She is no longer in her head. She is being protected by the spirits who help deaden her feelings. The figure of shame has returned, a mummy in a deep sleep. The goddess, painted on the lid of the coffin, is entreating her to wake up. She tells her the world is now safe. The grip that holds the child tight will show up again and again in my paintings. It manifests itself in my body by tightness in my chest and throat to the point that it becomes difficult for me to breathe when I try to speak about the rapes.

Not being able to speak or run or hide has been a recurring theme in my dreams since I was 3 years old. Painting has given me a way to sneak past the "thou shall not speak" demon.

Dream: I was at a street dance, walking around alone watching the activity. A sinister man approached me and attacked me. He pushed me down to the ground. I kept calling for help—at first barely a whisper—by the time I woke up, my cries for help were about normal speaking level. It required a great deal of effort to get even that loud.

If Looks Could Kill

This painting begins a series of small images done from a child's point of view. Dr. W. had suggested that I think, feel, or act like a child at some time during the next week. I translated that to: "Paint like a child." I found my smallest canvas and decided that a child would do a family portrait. In this scene, my father's feet are menacing because he is about to start kicking.

The dream and painting both say that there is a monster beneath the surface and it's a part of me. It is my first clue that there is a pool of anger beneath my cool facade. When I talk of the past with Dr. W., I always disclaim any anger, so this is an unsettling portent.

Dream: *I was riding with my husband, Dick, through the countryside. We came across an area of road that was flooded. It had become a lake. You could see that there had been a farm below the water. It was a sunny day and we took the detour. I kept watching the lake and noticed an area of great turbulence. I thought it was a horse running under the water but knew that was silly. As I watched, a great water snake (like the Loch Ness Monster) surfaced. I said, "Oh Dick, look—a monster. Did you see it?" I thought it was great that the lake had its own monster. We went on till we came to a farmhouse. We were supposed to clean it. It was quite disorderly. Dick did the laundry and I started to fold it. Then Dick's mom arrived. I asked if she knew about the monster and she said "Oh, yes, we know." It was obvious when I saw it that it was a benevolent monster in the sense that it wouldn't hurt me.*

I Never Actually Killed Daddy

This frozen moment happened when I was in my teens. My father had just beaten me in front of company. As he turned to leave the room, rage filled my heart. I got up from the floor and picked a knife off the counter. As I was bringing it down toward his back, I suddenly feared that I would miss a vital point. Then he would be truly angry and I would be sent to reform school. I didn't do it. That particular knife showed up in so many tense domestic situations that, for me, it became a family icon, imbued with horrific power.

Everybody Knows

Dream: *There was a big party. Jack was there and complaining because there weren't enough people at the party. He would have to speak to his enemies. I said it would take a big party, indeed, for him to be able to avoid his enemies.*

Sometimes as many as 10 kids would follow me, calling me names and throwing stones. This went on over a period of months when I was 11 and 12. I believe it was because they knew about the gang rape and blamed me for it. After all, they stoned harlots in the Bible stories and these kids had all been to Sunday school.

From the time of the rape until I was old enough to leave town, I felt surrounded by peers who scorned me. Long walks and reading sustained me and gave me a world away from their ridicule. However, the dream may also be suggesting that there are aspects of myself who are enemies and to whom I must speak.

When I Was Eleven

After the rape I was a different child. Bad things had happened before, but this was such a shock that I seemed to splinter apart. The separation was abrupt. This image shows my soul withdrawing to the corner of the room while another part of me turns into pure rage, leaving my physical self alone, uninhabited, and exposed. The boys were 15 to 17 years old. I remember their names still.

The dream is a good representation of my feelings about the boys and the futility of any defense I might have attempted. It also speaks to me about my own emotional numbness.

Dream: *I was being attacked by huge worms and I was stabbing them with a hunting knife. It was an overhand stab—using all my force. I felt that I hadn't really hurt them much, because they were too stupid to feel it.*

The Sex Object

Dream: *I was in a movie theater and a man or boy was rubbing against me. The harder I fought to get away, the more he seemed to like it. Finally, I started to scream and fight. He seemed to like it when I hurt him.*

Dr. W. suggested that I try to think, feel, or act like a man for an afternoon. I pulled out my largest canvas and painted as sloppy as I could under the premise that men have no control. It was fun to paint that way. This was the first of his many attempts to get me to relate to my inner masculine.

If I think of the man in the dream as my inner masculine, a part of my own psyche that I scorn and reject, I see that fighting him is like fighting a tarbaby. I will just become more deeply caught.

Me and My Shadow

Again, we talked of the inner masculine. I also began reading material that focused on the shadow or rejected aspects of one's personality. I was deeply moved and inspired by Sylvia Perera's *Descent to the Goddess: An Invitation for Women*, which I had just finished reading, twice. There is a great deal to be learned from the dark side of one's nature. This self-knowledge is well worth facing the fear and danger involved in the descent into the unconscious. The painting is concerned with my paralyzing fear of the beast within, rather than fear of the outer masculine.

The dream suggests that my inner madman will continue on his rampage until he gets my attention. He won't accept this powerless vehicle any longer. But there is hope. In fact, Dick is beside me working to stabilize the situation. The detective also represents a masculine power ready to help me harness the energy held by the madman.

Dream: *We were riding in the car, and Dick was tired, so he asked J. D. to drive. He started driving like a madman. We told him to slow down—he was hitting people. Then we realized he was doing it on purpose. He would even go back and hit them a second time. Somehow we were out of the car now and hiding the people he had hit—hoping he wouldn't hit them again. We knew he was after us and went out into the sagebrush, hoping we could go places the car couldn't. We knew there was little hope against a madman. The police came to investigate. The detective knelt down to look at the evidence and the bodies. A pair of arms came out of the space beside him and went around his neck. After he thought a while, he stood up and the arms fell away. He turned to another man and said, "There is a part of myself out there and it's out to get me."*

Dream: *I was getting set to leave the village with another woman (my sister?) and go back up into the hills where I lived. It was snowing. As we climbed the mountain, I slipped and I guess she did too. We were sliding down the mountain, and I hollered to her that we had to slow down and stop ourselves before we hit the trees. The next thing I knew, I had made it back to the village alone. I told them about the fall and the tree. I said maybe I am wrong, maybe she is alive, send out help and see. Then I passed out. When they came back they said that my sister had been shot. When I recovered physically, it became apparent that I had become crazy. I dressed strangely or not at all or anywhere in between. I talked gibberish. But one thing that pleased me is I discovered that when I held an audiotape in my hand I could hear the music. The person who took care of me saw that I could do this and thought it a good thing. After a while, the people got sick of me and wanted me thrown out of the village. They had a trial and things looked bad for me until my caretaker put an audiotape into my hands. It began to play. They were impressed and even though I was acting wild and looking worse, they decided I could stay. Later, I found a videotape that was 2 x 2 feet square and discovered that by wrapping myself around it I could see it. It was a video of my life.*

Me, Myself and I

The face I present to the world, my persona, is not an honest representation of my inner feelings. The angry inner me, my shadow, is desperate to kill off this false front. The mediating force between them is my self. I don't think it at all unusual to be of two minds on a subject or even three. However, most of us are taught to present a happy face to the world. Smile and the world will smile with you; cry and you cry alone. Show anger, and you are in deep trouble.

In this dream a part of myself is shot and killed, part has become insane, while a third aspect has become the caretaker. I am compensated by being given words and pictures so that I may tell my story. This is my first hint that I might be a writer as well as a painter and dreamer, but I didn't pick up on the clue at the time. These archetypal aspects of my self will continue to appear throughout this work as they act out the story of their growing awareness and integration.

Drowning in a Pool of Dreams

Dream: *I was carrying Dick because he was extremely weak. I was taking him down a long tunnel to safety. There were some men or demons following us and biting holes in us. While carrying Dick, I couldn't go fast enough to avoid their bites, and I was getting weaker. I thought maybe we would do better if Dick walked. But it was too late. They had bit our legs so much that we couldn't walk. It was like being pecked to death by chickens.*

I wanted to express my feelings of being overwhelmed and exposed by the past eight months of painting, dreams, and therapy. I was relieved to see that among the spectators, neither my therapist nor my husband were laughing at my precarious position. As we discussed the image, Dr. W. pointed out that I had done 10 paintings in the past two months, so I had reached my goal of overcoming the creative block. We could stop if I felt overwhelmed. However, considering the nature of the paintings, I wanted his continued support while I explored these dangerous depths.

The masculine force in my dream and in my life has become weak from lack of exercise. Instead of being a helpful part of myself, it has become a burden that allows me to feel defeated by small cowardly demons.

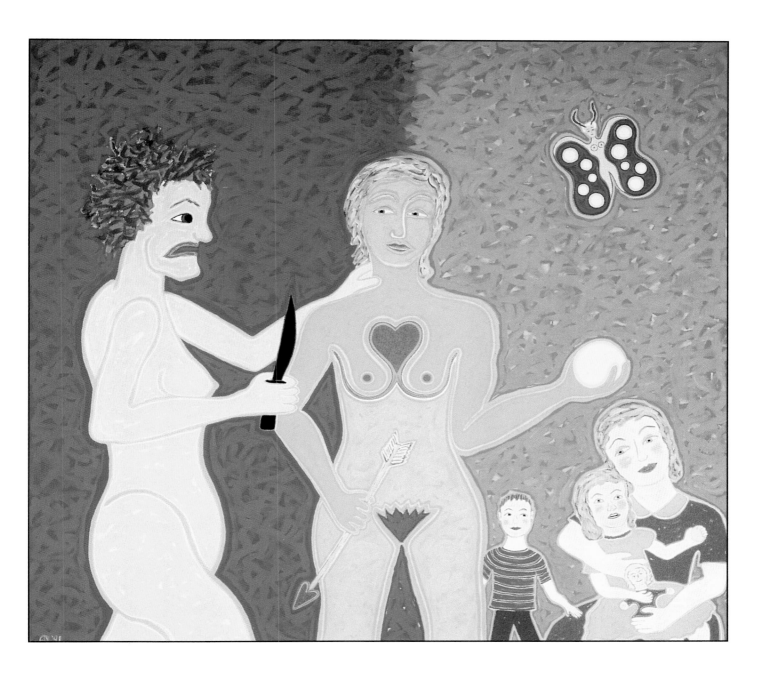

An Inner Portrait

Dr. W. suggested that I ask my inner self what she wants. In fact, why not ask all of my inner selves what they want? I see the figure in the middle as the one who wishes to be centered. She balances the masculine (arrow) with the feminine (golden ball). On the left is the angry self from the earlier image, *Me, Myself and I.* Having been driven deep into the unconscious, she now wants to get my attention. Perhaps she is trying to tell me that I need a driving force to keep from stagnation. The inner masculine is small and tentative. I think he just wants to get into the picture. The child wants to be loved, and a caring part of myself wants to love her. The final self in this image is the transformative free spirit in the form of a butterfly. She wants her day in the sun.

Daddy's Home and Boy Are You Going to Get It Now

My dad was big and heavy. This image doesn't do justice to his actual size. However, I often experienced him as 300 pounds of raging bull coming at me with his arms flailing. Of course, he wasn't always this way, but fear and pain create a lasting impression.

One of my earliest memories of Daddy is when he returned from the war. He put me on his shoulders and carried me around the house. It was exciting to be so high until he dropped me. As I fell, my head hit the radiator. After that I would scream when he entered the room. He sat by me on the couch with his hand over my mouth while I screamed. We did not bond in the usual way.

Monsters in the Night

I am still hiding on top of the wardrobe. It is easier for a child to believe a monster came in the night, than to admit someone who should love her had been the source of pain and shame.

The dream and painting are both frightening images from the unconscious. The light coming in the door scares me as much as the rest of it. Dick seems to represent an inner strength that can help me face up to the monsters.

Dream: *I was a young girl. I went into my bedroom to take a nap. He was there. After I fell asleep a dog started licking my vulva. I couldn't wake up but I was sure it was a dog and was afraid it would bite me and eat me. It felt physically exciting, but at the same time mentally repulsive and quite frightening. After a while, Dick came in the room. I was afraid he would be disgusted by what he saw. But he just laid down beside me and put his arm around my shoulders. As he held me, the dog melted away.*

2. Masculine/Feminine

Approaching the Wasteland

Dream: *I was out for a walk in a sort of underworld. It was a dark, tree-lined pathway with houses, but few people. Dick showed up and was walking with me. It was pleasant walking and talking together. As we approached the outside world, we hung on to each other tightly. We went out into the light and found it a nasty world. There were all kinds of nasty, deformed men accosting us. One tried to pee on us. The sun was shining, and this world seemed to have potential if we could get past this ugly area at the entrance. We climbed a ladder attached to a decrepit building and looked around. We decided that our best bet was to go back into the tunnel, if we could. Otherwise, we had a long unpleasant journey ahead of us out through the wasteland.*

As I painted this dream, I changed the identity of the man accompanying me. Since it is a psychological wasteland, I decided I would prefer to have a psychologist with me, to help me survive the trip. He gives me support and encouragement, but I must carry my own baggage. We discussed this image in the next session and decided that, in the wasteland of the soul, the canteen would carry hope.

We come out of a tunnel into the light, a birth, and find it tough going. That describes the therapy process, so far, quite well. I now have my masculine side to support me as we go forward, since I really do not want to retreat into the darkness. Dr. W. was uneasy at being depicted beside me, both of us unclothed, until I explained that clothes are seldom worn in archetypal reality.

Trying to Explain the Need to Feel

I felt inarticulate when trying to explain to Dr. W. that I seem cut off from my emotions. Often an emotion will hit me three days after the event that triggered it, far too late for an appropriate response. I know intuitively that I need to be more connected. There is a desire to cut through to the heart of the problem, to let the pressure bleed out. Perhaps then I could talk about it.

Dropping frozen memories into the ocean seems a gentle way to thaw them, releasing the emotions, now that I am safe to experience them. The safety is the result of several factors: 40 years have passed, I have strengths now I didn't have then, there is no longer anyone in my life who would hurt me, and I have a compassionate professional to guide and support me. It will be a slow process, with no easy outs allowed. What is pulled apart must be rebuilt using the same memories, now transformed by removal of the toxic residue.

Dream: *I was trapped inside a huge skull made of ice. Big machines were taking sections of the sides and hauling them away to drop into the ocean. I tried to climb up the side and out a hole (the eye?) to avoid the machines. Someone was with me. We got to the ledge near the hole, and a man walked toward us. I hoped he would pull us through, but I think he was going to push us back. Later in the night I dreamed that my head was smashed in and had to be rebuilt.*

My First Memory

Dream: *I was a little girl. A friend had been cruel to me and I was going away to be alone. The person called out behind me that she would never be cruel to a good girl or one who had any talent. I kept going. My legs gave out and I fell in the middle of the street. I dragged myself the rest of the way and hid behind a railing on the other side of the road. A voice said, "In an emergency, one thing was for sure, the Almighty left the body."*

My playmate is waiting outside on the porch while her grandfather molests me. My first conscious memory combines violation by the masculine with betrayal by the feminine. She must have known what was happening, as I am sure she must have also been a casualty. To blame the child is, of course, ridiculous but at the time I did. On the way home I was sad because I had lost my first friend. I could never go back to play with her again.

The dream reveals that I see myself as powerless, betrayed, and godless. I'm sinned against because I am a sinner. I can't support myself in the dream. In real life, I have had mysterious pains and numbness in my legs for many years. There was no medical explanation. It was my psyche speaking to me through my body, using the language of symbol. At the age of 3, in my panic, I lost my connection to The One Spirit. Since then, I have vacillated between hiding and seeking.

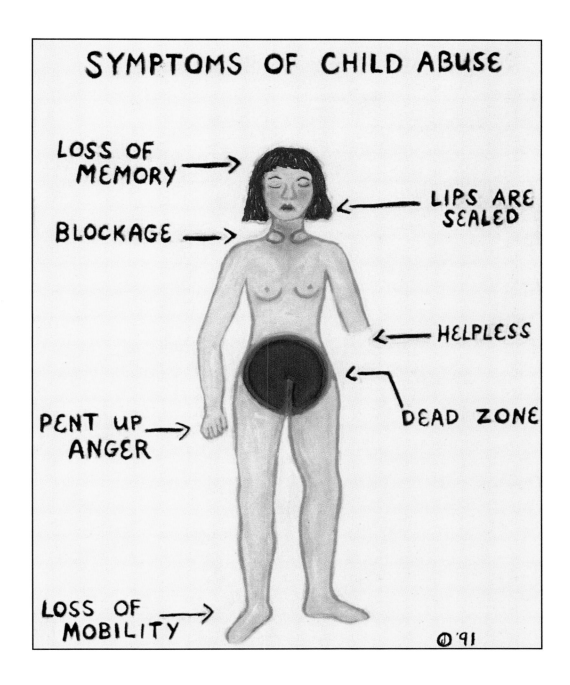

SYMPTOMS OF CHILD ABUSE

LOSS OF MEMORY →

BLOCKAGE →

LIPS ARE SEALED

HELPLESS

DEAD ZONE

PENT UP ANGER →

LOSS OF MOBILITY →

⏀ '91

Symptoms of Child Abuse

My intention in this painting was to make the figure like a textbook illustration of all the real symptoms of child abuse. They are all symptoms with which I have direct experience. There are few events in this book that I haven't carried consciously all my life. What I wasn't conscious of was how it colored my view of myself and the world.

The dead zone represents a symptom that had a great effect on my life. By the age of 10, I had sworn many times never to have children. I was afraid I would have a daughter and be unable to protect her from the evils of the world. When as an adult I found myself unable to bear a child, I felt more relief than regret. The dream speaks about my fears of family life and the vulnerability of all involved.

Dream: *I was a shy and withdrawn woman. I felt unattractive. I met a man who I felt was wonderful. He was creative, a builder and designer. We became close and once in a moment of weakness, I told him I loved him. To my amazement he returned my feeling. Anyway, we were married and had a lot of fun together. Then we had a child. When the child was 5 or 6, the man became unhappy. He was sitting by a window. His pants were around his knees. He was crying and saying he was no good for the child. I sat in front of him to protect him from the world. I was facing the window and listening to him. Then I heard a gun. I realized he had blown his brains out. I just faced the window and cried.*

A Meeting of Opposites

The opposite forces meet under the shelter of the tree of life. The serpent, a symbol of perpetual self–renewal, is a mediating and healing force between them. Are they holding images of their own inner masculine and feminine sides? Perhaps they are mirroring back what they see or only what the other wishes to see. The main figures may be halves of one being. It has such numerous qualities that I can only speculate on the possibilities inherent in the image.

Although the masculine potential is big, the dreamer keeps him in a small square box. I am willing to nourish him but I don't wish to admit my interdependence with this kind, gentle, creative force even though I am of the same tree. I need to be willing to kiss the toad to liberate the prince, not theoretically, but in real life.

Dream: *There was a fat man in a small square box hanging on the end of a tree limb (like a bud). He loved me and wanted to be with me, but I was repulsed by him. Somehow he got me to stand close enough to the tree so that he could suckle my breasts. After that I thought of him often, and cared for him, but I kept it to myself as I still found him repulsive. He was gentle and kind. He made wonderful paintings that told the stories of the world. I was a painter too and could see my paintings laid out on the ground. I viewed them from high in the sky. I knew I would eventually accept the man and release him from the box.*

Now They All Know

When I read about the local conference on sexual abuse in the paper, it seemed appropriate to offer my paintings as an educational tool. I hadn't thought of how exposed I would feel. The experience reactivated childhood feelings of isolation and contamination. My unconscious self handled the resulting emotional turmoil by spilling coffee in my lap so that I would have to leave the conference.

The man in my dream is in reality a tree planter and works for the greater good. He is a wonderful model for my inner masculine, a rugged outdoorsman who performs willingly when called to serve. That he is sustained by the trees he has planted tells me that I, too, will be nourished by the fruit of the seeds I plant. The dream is a call to service.

Dream: *There was a big, rough-looking man. He was being required to take a long journey carrying a large load. Only a third of the load was his own personal stuff needed on the trip. The rest was being carried for the greater good of the community that he had always lived apart from. He wasn't a true hermit, just a loner. But when he got the call to carry the load, he put it on and started down the road. Along the way, at designated stops, he would have a cup of water with a green gelatin in it—the gelatin came from the wayside trees. One result of this trip is that he got in great shape, which no one seemed to care about except him—if he did. His journey was being watched by elders on a video monitor.*

Banished

Dream: *I was in an underground labyrinth. There was ice everywhere including underfoot. I was surrounded by thin ice. There were some pathways that had thicker ice, and I was running along them as fast as I could. There was a man with a knife. It was Dr. W., chasing me. He kept hollering at me to stop and he would guide me to safety. I knew I was surrounded by 25,000 miles of thin ice, but he seemed the larger threat. I kept running.*

Dr. W. asked me to henceforth wait in the outer room until he was ready to begin. For a year, I had been coming into the session area while he finished his paper work in the adjacent office. I was extremely embarrassed to think I had been overstepping the boundary. Since I had just shown these revealing paintings for the first time, I was feeling exposed, ripe for an overreaction. My feelings of rejection and anger came to the surface, overwhelming me. I felt possessed by the anger. I went to the library and read three books about therapy to understand what was happening. Reading about transference allowed me to realize that this "way out of proportion" reaction was useful to the growth process. That knowledge allowed me to return the next week, but it was six months before I could face him with equanimity. It was an incredibly fruitful time.

I perceive the knife as a symbol of power, rather than as a threat, because even in my fear I know he wants to help me. It was commitment to the process and my growing trust in the relationship that allowed me to stop running and face my fear.

It's OK. It's Safe to Scream

The hardest thing I have done since starting therapy was showing up for this session. I expressed my anger and other feelings immediately. Rather than getting involved in the trigger that set me off, Dr. W. simply asked if I wanted to breath into those feelings. The deep breathing led to screaming long and loud, and then to laughing, more screaming, some babbling, and more laughing. And all the while he was there saying it was OK. I remember once touching his face in amazement. I thought that must be how a baby feels after screaming her lungs out to look up and see a concerned, caring face filling her vision.

This dream certainly expresses my sense of being overrun by my emotions. Maybe it means that I have learned a big lesson, that my fear of rejection was as big as a bus. Having experienced the intensity of that feeling so deeply and survived has reduced my fear to mere car size.

Dream: *There were two buses. One was parked, and the other one was coming in to park in front of it. As it swept into the space, it hit a pedestrian and he flew 20 feet through the air. It kept happening over and over. It was a lesson for the pedestrian, trying to teach him not to get too close to a bus. On the last one he backed up quickly and was hit by a car instead.*

Dream: (*This is the end of a long involved escape dream.*) *I ran on. I was being chased. Someone hollered encouragement, saying to lay down my burden ... my mother. She should run for herself. We should be escaping together but not with me carrying her. But she couldn't run, because she was a huge dead rabbit. I was running to catch a bus and thus escape our pursuers but I could see no bus ahead. In fact, there was no road.*

Memories of Mother

The intense feelings of rejection that have been with me for the past two weeks have turned my thoughts to Mother. She caught the bus at noon for the 20–mile ride to the city where she worked. Even when I was in school, I sensed her walking out the door. When I was 35, my parents moved to the town that had become my home. Until then, I had kept 3,000 miles between us. As a child, I had begged Mother to stay. As an adult, I begged her to leave. I don't know which was more painful. My relation-ship to her is equal parts guilt and longing.

The rabbit is one of the symbols of The Goddess, The Great Mother. That it is dead in the dream caused me to question my connection to the feminine creative force. I know I am uncomfortable with women in general and my mother in particular. This realization convinced me to seek out a women's therapy group in an effort to embrace the trepidation I felt around women. We had all experienced childhood trauma. Most of the group of six women had been together for over three years, so I felt like an outsider. I decided that was a good thing, since being an outcast was another wound that needed to be opened and explored.

The Devouring Mother

When I was a child, I experienced my mother as unobtainable. Her parents had separated when she was 8 years old, so her mother had also been unavailable. There was a chasm of unfulfilled love on the maternal line. This image expresses my feeling of being eaten alive by her when my parents retired near my home. They wanted me to take care of them, to mother them. I am appalled at myself for showing my mother in this light. However, in the process of therapy, I can't censor feelings that are difficult to face, indeed, the crux of many problems.

It was a terrible conflict for me when my parents retired here. They wanted me to be attentive: to come to dinner several times a week, drop by daily, invite them to dinner, shovel snow off their roof, take care of their dog, play cards, and tell them everything that was happening in my life. For the first time, my parents seemed interested in me. We were a family. Then I realized that I was being crowded out of my life. Part of me was cooperating fully and part of me was going bonkers.

Dream: *I was reading a letter that had several enclosures. My mom was reading over my shoulder. She was crowding me and I was quite annoyed with her. I gave her part of the letter hoping she would back off and read it. But she kept crowding me—wanting the part that I had.*

Not Worth the Powder to Blow Her Up With

Dream: *He wanted to lay down with the big cat instead of the kitty. The dream is the story of how it ate him. It started when he filled the animal house with crushed nuts. Then he went into the cat cage (cats don't eat nuts, so of course they were still hungry). He found a palette knife. It was in the drawer of a painting of a sideboard. Someone showed him how to use it and then things really got wild.*

"You aren't worth the powder to blow you up with," was one of my dad's choice remarks to us kids. Building self-esteem in his kids was a concept that never entered his mind.

When I awoke from this dream I immediately went to the store and bought a bigger palette knife. Painting with a palette knife seems like switching on masculine energy. Instead of using just the fingers and wrist action to paint, suddenly I am using my whole arm. I felt like I had let a tiger loose when I discovered this way to embody the masculine force in my art. It releases a highly emotional energy. It isn't surprising to me that the image is self-destructive, since most of my repressed anger is directed inward.

The Face Behind the Mask

So often when a child tries to tell what has been happening, she is not believed because the monster that she sees is hidden behind a civilized mask. In this painting she is trying to tell her protector about the mask that is hiding the true nature of the man.

As I drew this image, even *I* wanted to stop her from telling. I didn't want to paint it. I thought of covering it up and doing something else over it. I left it on the easel for two days. This dream convinced me to go ahead with the painting because I realized that I was the censor spoken of in the dream.

Dream: *The art gallery was going to censor my work. This made me angry enough to say that they would show it all or find someone else. I wouldn't allow them to censor my pieces. They said maybe they could get someone to take my place.*

The Pain Tells Her She's Alive

Dream: A man was trying to put me at ease so that I could tell him something. I was afraid that someone would hear us and shoot me before I could tell him. We blocked the windows and turned on a loud fan, so no one could hear. Then I became worried that if I told him, they would kill him for knowing.

After discussing the child in *The Face Behind the Mask*, Dr. W. suggested that I ask my inner child what she wants. This image is the answer. From looking at her, I decided that her needs would not be met by rocking her and telling her fairy tales. She wants the truth to be told. She wants to express her deepest feelings so that she can be truly alive again. Her pain convinced me that I must show my work. It is for this part of myself, the child Janie, who has always wanted "to tell" that I am going through all of this again. Whenever I want to back out of sharing my art and my life, I remember the impact this realization had on me. I reaffirm the promise I made to speak for the child I was and for the children who are now suffering.

I have felt so close, lately, to the child who experienced these horrible events. Her fears about telling have incredible resonance in my life, whether I am awake or asleep.

Consumed by Hatred

Five of my last six paintings have had knives in them. This was still bothering me, so I discussed it again with Dr. W. I told him that I had bought a dozen knives and placed them around the house in an effort to penetrate their significance. He suggested that I choose my favorite and paint with it. I scoffed and said one couldn't paint with a butcher knife. Later, in the studio, I thought, "I am paying this man a lot of money. I had better follow his advice." This painting is the first one painted with a butcher knife. It clearly speaks of my hatred for those who hurt me. By the age of 9, I had become like a broadcast beacon of hatred. I hated everything and everyone around me, except my dog. When I was 22, and recently married, I was sitting in my kitchen hating those who had hurt me. Suddenly I realized that I was getting sick from hating them. They were 200 miles away and had no idea what I was thinking and they probably felt just fine. If I continued to hate them, it would mean they had won. I stopped hating, on a conscious level. It was like turning off a faucet.

The explosives in the basement of this old house speak to me of my old hatred. It is still there beneath the surface. As much as it frightens me, I have to deal with it before it blows me apart. First, the knives tried to tell me and now the dream tells me to wake up—pay attention—and work with this.

Dream: *I was in the basement of a huge house—very old. I was watching a highly explosive substance bubbling up out of vents and spreading across the floor. Soon the house would blow sky high. I woke up. When I slept again, I had the same dream. Both times I woke before it blew up.*

3. I Feel

Beyond All Reason

This painting was executed with a butcher knife, as are many from this point onwards. The image reminds me of an earlier painting, *The Sex Object*. Now the woman is feeling and reacting, rather than being the passive object. When traumatized, survival often depends on the ability to numb the pain, both physical and emotional. However, your feelings are all connected, as the pain is stuffed in a box, so is the pleasure. When the shame is hidden, the ability to feel pride is lost, too.

I am surrounded by peril and unable to help myself or summon help. The danger finally catches up with me, then violation. What allows me to survive is that I am made so degraded that I pose no threat to the villains. The dream reveals that deeply imprinted unworthiness kept me silent. Painting with the knife is causing an eruption of emotions that is both daunting and electrifying.

Dream: *I was at the home of the leader of my therapy group. She was having a party. Suddenly, the kitchen was on fire. We tried to leave by ladders and mine broke. I was left stranded on the roof. Then I was in another house and it caught on fire. I called 911, but the line was busy. I found a fire extinguisher, but it was old (an inch of dust) and we didn't know how to work it. The fire spread. I went down a long dark hall into my dark room to get my things and leave. When I went in my room, I was hit on the head. A man pushed me down and started to rape me from behind. He was giving lessons to a boy with him. He said it was important to make me feel like an asswipe in case they decided to let me live. They would decide that later.*

Guardian Spirit

The emotional intensity realized while painting with a knife gives me pause to wonder how I got through such terrible times. Here is my Guardian Spirit who supported me. She is my funny, free-flying self who spent her childhood in trees and on country roads, alone and full of dreams.

While I have been delving into the past, my present day Guardian Spirit, a real life friend and partner, has been steadfast in his support. The lines of communication that are allowing me to share my secrets are also open to share our dreams with one another. A year ago I dreamed that I could not allow the branches of our trees to touch. Now their meeting adds to my well-being. The dream also reminds me of the inner masculine, the animus, who shares my quest.

Dream: *Dick had found a diamond wedding band to go with my other ring. The diamonds were all on the underside. As he gave it to me, another woman said, "That is a marvelous diamond you have, and I don't mean the one on your finger." I said, "Yes, I know." We were both referring to Dick.*

Reaching for Help

Dream: *I was in a dark hospital room. I got out of bed but was weak and fell to the floor. It was too dark to be sure, but I thought that there was blood pouring from my face after my fall. I thought I had gone through all this stuff years ago. Why do I have to do it again? Will this time be a cure, or is it the wound that never heals?*

During this time in my therapy, I was more aware of and alarmed by my feelings. I felt depressed, agitated, lost, and alone. In fact, I felt so bad that I called my therapist and asked what was happening to me. I described my feelings and he said, "That's anxiety. You said you wanted to have aware-ness of your feelings. So what's the problem?" Cold, but true. I realized that this was something I had to experience. He had helped me get to this point and it was going to get worse before it got better.

Sunk in Gloom

Dream: *I was washing a huge black velvet floor, but I didn't have enough water. I was on my hands and knees scrubbing. It was OK, except I didn't know where I could get more water.*

Once I realized that I needed to go ahead and feel low down and blue, I surrendered to it. This picture captures the intensity of the lost–and–alone quality that absorbed me. I felt this way throughout much of my childhood.

In the painting I appear to be surrounded by water, but my mood and mind are as black as the velvet in the dream. Depression is con-nected to the hopelessness of having a huge impossible job to do.

Go Make Your Daddy Happy

"Go make your daddy happy" were the words Mom said when she sent me into the lion's den. I began this painting while thinking of my mother. I wanted her love and protection, but what I felt from her was disregard. No one could make Daddy happy. I didn't want to go in there.

The dream tells me that I have an obligation to do my part for the children. I need to give the protection I had wanted. My involvement will be distant, rather than on a personal level, but can have an effect nonetheless. I have always been afraid to speak in public, in private, too. I believe I am being called to face that fear.

Dream: *I was in my hometown in a beauty parlor having my hair done. I told them that I was traveling and talking about my childhood in that town. I pointed to the house across the street and said I grew up in that house. Bad things happened there. Violent things. These days the state can take children from a home like that. Sometimes that is enough to change things—even if the child returns home soon.*

Learning to Fly

Dr. W. and I had been congratulating one another on how much work we had done and on how well things were moving along. He said, "And someday maybe you will know what you are going to paint before you paint it, instead of this weird kind of channeling that you do." I nodded my head in agreement at the time. But the next morning I woke up in alarm, "Weird kind of channeling!?!" Oh my God, that was the one thing I was confident that I was doing right! I was really upset. In fact, this was probably transference at work again, an out–of–proportion reaction to a perceived rejection. By the end of the day, I had worked through the conflict and realized that I was doing it exactly right, but his remark caused me to question myself, my process of painting, and then, my trust in him. If he seemed to be so wrong about something I felt was important, could I really trust him? My way of discovering how I felt about him was to trust my weird kind of channeling. I stood before the easel and asked my inner self how she felt about Dr. W. Does she trust him? In this image I see that he perceives where I am now and where he would like me to be someday. This means that he is not just sitting there recording. He has a vision. I do trust him.

Metamorphosis

In the previous painting *Learning to Fly*, I appeared to be bound, but maybe I was simply in a cocoon. While painting *Metamorphosis*, I felt like I was bursting free of constraints.

The dream speaks to me of the metamorphosis of a book into a library and of building on the past to create the future. Recently, I have begun noting my thoughts about the paintings, a small beginning towards preserving my personal heritage.

Dream: *A man was asking a fraternal organization to give him a book. It was the only one on their bookshelf. I was trying to convince them not to give away their heritage. I told the man he should borrow it. Read it and bring it back to be the first one in the library. I said he would be just the man to build the library.*

She Hates

Dream: *There was a pickup truck with a camper. The truck ran mad and became a homicidal maniac. It locked its owner in the shower of the camper and turned on the water, drowning him. The truck fell in love with another pickup and chased her through the night. But whenever it saw people, it would go out of its way to run over them.*

Allowing myself to really experience melancholy, as well as angry feelings, has led me into a deep funk. This creature was at the bottom of the pit. She is myself who has been kept bottled up since I was 22, since the day I turned off my hate. She who hates is painted in the colors of *Rape*, red and green and black. She is the inarticulate rage of that child grown into a deadly wrath.

My homicidal maniac has me locked away drowning in my subcon-scious hatred. I seek love but I run off anyone who might get close to me. I think this hating self needs to be acknowledged, even honored, and her energy redirected so that she can be safely released from the pit.

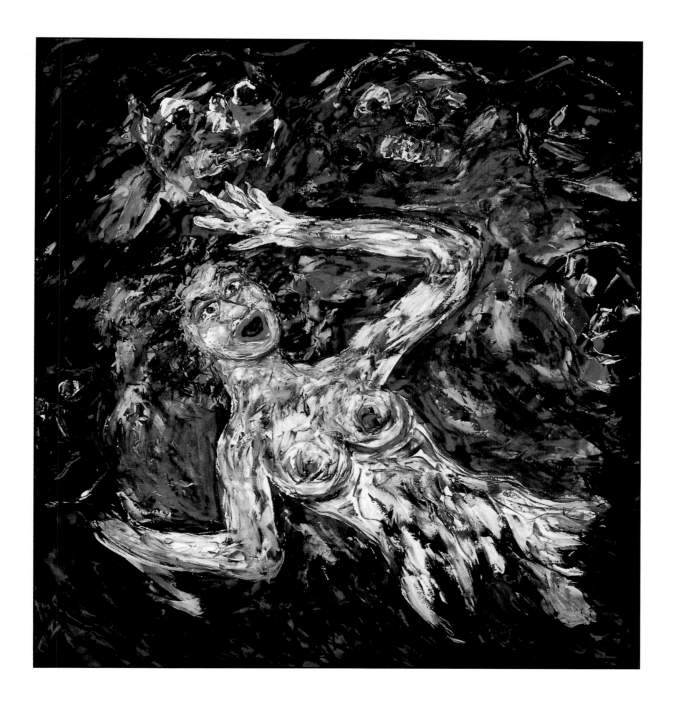

Fear

Today I received a copy of a journal that had published four of my paintings. Below them, in print, was my secret for all the world to see. My heart started to go a mile a minute and I was hot and cold all over; abso–lute FEAR. So I went to my studio and painted the feeling. The five ghoulish faces around me go back to the early image, *Rape*. The experience of that rape is the source of my greatest fears.

My fear is represented by the dream creature, bat/fly. It keeps me silent. At first I saw my silence as a beautiful butterfly, later I recognized it as the source of the poison that was destroying me.

Dream: *At first I thought it was a butterfly. It landed on my left hand and bit it. Then it flew to my right hand, sunk its teeth in and held on. It looked like a miniature bat. I tried to ask for help to get it off me, but I couldn't speak. The only sound I could make was "arrgh." I knew it was the venom from this bat/fly that had robbed me of speech.*

Melting the Cage of Ice

Dream: *I was driving a snowmobile over huge mounds of dirty, rutted snow. I was going much too fast. I couldn't see over the next rise or how deep the ruts were. I think I crashed. The next thing I know I am in a house. Someone is putting boxes of frozen meat on the counter. One is labeled "guts and gizzards, 8 years old, Emily." Another box contains a young woman. I want to leave this house but feel I must stay to investigate. I decide not to eat anything in this house—especially meat.*

I was experiencing an emotional time this month. I had 81 paintings on display at a gallery in my community. Many people viewed the show in tears and thanked me for telling their story, or their sister's, wife's, mother's, daughter's, or son's story. It was becoming difficult to maintain a cool facade. I rely on Dr. W. and the therapy process to help me with these intense emotions.

It would seem natural for this exhibit to be a culmination of my therapeutic experience. However, the dream suggests that I not be so fast in my assumptions. The child may have been at the meat of the matter, but now there is the young woman to consider. I still have much to learn.

ALL RIGHT!

There is a wonderful feeling of victory at having broken the long years of silence about the rapes and beatings of my childhood. In doing the public exhibit of this art, I found that I spoke not only for myself but for hundreds of others in my community. That is not a happy reality, but there is a real freedom in acknowledging the truth.

The dream had such a sense of immediacy that, in the morning, I went to my favorite coffeehouse bookstore and roamed the shelves looking for the gift from my dream self. I found *Charlotte: Life or Theater?*, an extraordinary autobiographical play, written and painted by Charlotte Salomon in a two-year period, 1940–1942. She died in Auschwitz in 1943 at the age of 26. In an incredibly moving tour de force, she painted 769 images; a grim, ironic view of her own existence and the dark side of life. She is a hero who fills my heart with her courage and determination. The book is both a reward and an inspiration.

Dream: *A gift was found in a used bookstore. It was given to me inscribed, "With thanks to a woman's artist. The future will find books filled with pictures."*

4. The Burden of the Past Is the Seed of the Future

Opening the Wounds

The week after my local exhibit was over, I hung two exhibits at universities in an urban center 100 miles away. The newspapers have responded with articles that amaze me with their graphic language. They boldly address the issues involved. There is no turning back for me, no return to the closet. But I still want to say it wasn't so bad, others had worse, I survived. My pain was small, theirs was great. Does the desire to hide behind a mask grow from shame or pride?

The painting is inspired by the dream; however, I decided that it would be best to cut open the hidden wounds and let them heal with the scars on the outside. When I faced my fear of speaking by presenting a slide lecture, it was both a real and symbolic opening of the wounds.

Dream: *I was trying to explain the three different kinds of pain that one must live with. The person I was talking to was someone detached, like a doctor. I said there is the pain caused by living under a great weight and the pain of having many cuts all over the body that heal over but leave terrible scars on the inside of the skin. The worst is living with all the bones being broken and pretending everything is OK.*

Baptized by Fire and Water

Fire and water fill my dreams. I am trying to find my center between the fire above and the water below. Both have the power to destroy, purify, and renew. Fire is a force of consciousness, masculine, and assigned to the yang principle. Water is yin, unconscious and feminine. I wish for my heart to be open to the healing powers of both fire and water.

In the dream, the water claims me, but not before I find my whole self: woman, man, and child. We were filled with grace as we accepted the water.

Dream: *I was in a ship. It broke apart. They actually jettisoned a portion in an effort to save the rest, but it didn't help. She was filling with water and going down fast. Many people gave up and put their faces in the water to get it over with. One man talked and laughed to the end. I saw a person (who kept changing between woman or man) holding a child. I swam over to them and said, "I'm so glad to see you." We all smiled at one another. The water came up to our chins, and our heads were against the ceiling. I put my arms around them. I said, "I am happy I met you." Then we were drowned.*

The Sacrament

Dream: *There was a pool of blood in the size and shape of a double bed. Flowers made from tissues were floating on it. They were white but edged with red. I knew that they were a beautiful sight but that all of the blood came from the violation of my body. There was terrible pain. But as I wiped the blood from me with tissue and threw it away, it formed this beautiful bed of roses.*

The red rose is a symbol of wounds, of love, and of mystic rebirth. The rose with its thorns speaks to me of the beauty of accepting my own truth. In laying open the well of pain, shame, and grief hidden in my heart, I allowed a cleansing. *The Sacrament* is a sign of the compassion and grace conveyed by that cleansing.

While I slept, this dream seemed appalling and full of pain. As I awoke, I came to cherish its truth and beauty. My dream self has sent me an image of acceptance. It symbolizes my emancipation from the past, a release activated by delving into, accepting, and dispersing that which held me enthralled. I am no longer in the grip of the fate worse than death.

The Offering

The impact of sharing my art continues to affect my dreams. As an artist I must be honest and open in order to fulfill the function of reflecting our common soul. This is especially so when I am embarrassed by its content or frightened by its intensity.

I am sacrificing my face, the mask that has protected me, to nourish those who follow. In our discussions about this imagery, Dr. W. brought up the concept of service. He spoke of how important it has proven to be for people recovering from emotional traumas (and addictions) to share their gift of health. What is given freely to others deepens in one's self.

Dream: *I was sitting by Dick in a theater but felt I didn't really have the right to be there, so I moved away. But he drew me back to him. We left the building. I found myself on a path through a barren land. Then I went through an area where a few small trees had been planted in an effort at reforestation. From there I could see down a long steep mountain to a wide river below. There was a long spit of land that almost reached across the river. I went out there. I knew that the land was always washing away—dangerous. I wondered how I would get the rest of the way across. All this while I knew Dick and others were following me. I made camp and built a fire. I laid down with my head in the flames. I knew that my face was the fuel to cook the meal. A grill was laid over my face with meat on it. It looked like a mask. When it was removed my face would be gone.*

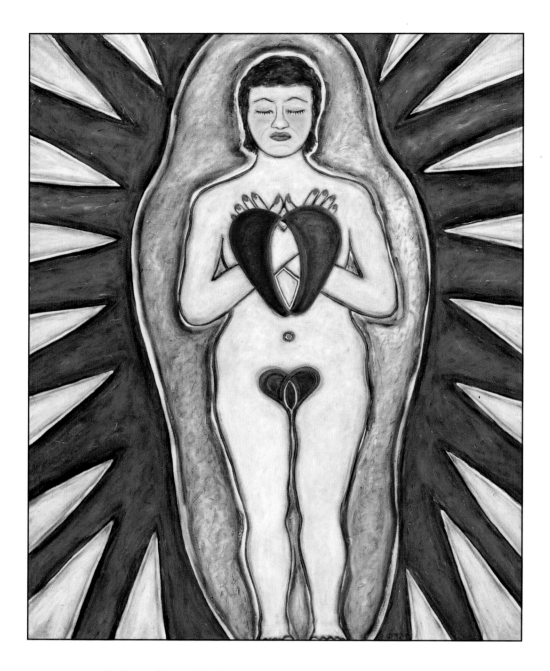

Mandala of a Whole Person

Dream: *There was a mature mother and a daughter who was a young woman. Together they were raising a baby girl. They were accepting, maybe pleased, with the fact that there were no men in their lives. But then a man shows up to propose to the mother. He comes with a truck load of daisies and maple tree limbs. This means he has to be considered. He creates a cozy house of four rooms. It is square, but built inside a round cave with a view out one side–overlooking a plain. The whole house is reflected in its ceiling, so it is doubled. She ponders his proposal. He tells her to accept only if she feels they will find joy together. She decides yes. There was an unseen visitor in the wings who decides to leave without making himself known so they can be alone for their honeymoon. He speeds away (flying) across the plain to the river and flies low along the water. He sees all the strange things traveling by water.*

Dr. W. introduced me to a meditation centered on the heart. I felt and accepted the support of all who had gone before me. They are represented by the rays coming in toward me like hands reaching to touch my heart and connect me to the Whole.

I am very happy with this dream of wholeness; the feminine triad, the masculine with his marvelous offering, the house—square within the circle—doubled and filled with joy. And there is a promise of more mystery beneath the surface.

The Prince Is Hidden

I need to accept the toadlike aspects of myself. Perhaps that is why I wish to share my experience with sex offenders. If I find some aspect of them redeemable, then I might be able to forgive and redeem parts of myself. At the root, we suffer a similar illness, but they are actively contagious. A probation officer who took an offender to see my show said the offender cried, a rare show of emotion. If my work plants a seed of empathy, perhaps it will evolve into compassion toward others. That possibility compels me to make the effort.

The toad prince, my despised inner masculine self, has heart. He maintains that there is more to him than just a reflection of past assailants. Beneath that image hides the mentors who taught me to pursue literature, philosophy, art, self-knowledge, and self-defense. Last year I dreamed of the masculine being kept in a small square box. I thought he couldn't be released until I was willing to kiss the toad. Apparently that time has come.

Dream: *There was a man who looked like a toad. He was searching for another man, a prince, handsome, charming, and afraid. The woman hid the prince in a sliding hidden space in a bookshelf. When the toadlike man showed up, I found myself strangely drawn to him. I kissed him and felt a great love for him.*

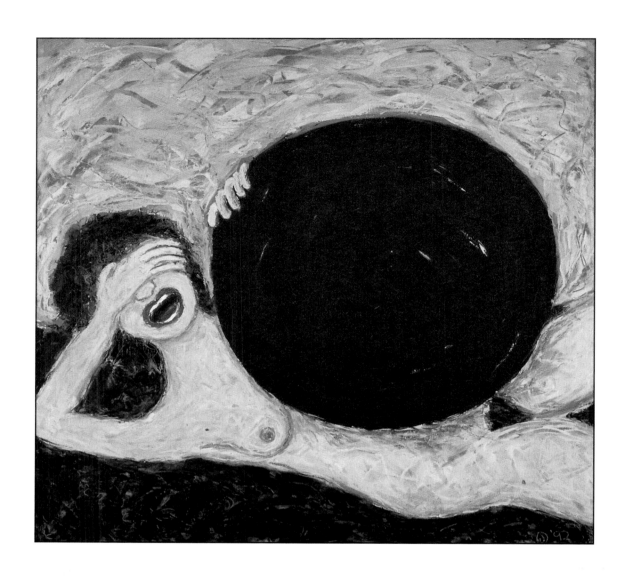

Unacknowledged Feelings

Dream: *There was a wooden rack with washing hung on it. The laundry was all the pieces of truth. The little truths covered up the big ones. Suddenly I saw through the smaller ones I'd been looking at and said, "I hate him. I hate you?" (Something about hating—it was very intense, but I've forgotten it now.) The voice as I woke up said, "That is his truth, not yours." Later that night I dreamt there was a nun with a bad habit. She was fiddling with a clock, a time bomb. She said it was a 90s version of a joke.*

I felt a heavy weight pressing in on me. I didn't know what was getting me down, so I decided to paint the feeling itself. In doing that I realized that I couldn't identify feelings that I refused to acknowledge.

My dream self quickly refused to remember and acknowledge her feelings. I am warned that my "good self" may be playing a dangerous joke. And the joke's on me. By nicely maintaining that I am without anger, I have just stored away trouble. It is apt to blow up in my face, unless I start releasing it a bit at time.

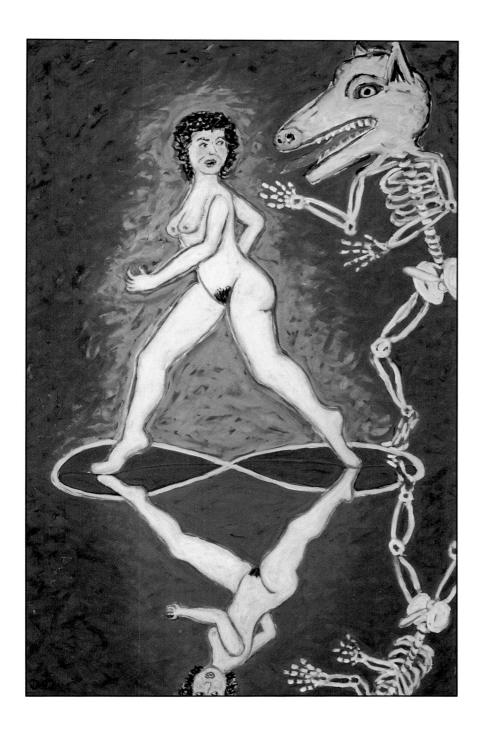

Ever After

The endless quality of fear and dread traveling down through time is reflected in this image. I am determined to quit running and face my fears.

There has been a breach in my defenses leading to a change in the status quo. Although my first reaction was to hide, I knew I was going to have to come up with a new approach to life. It was good for me to tell my story to the offenders. The experience has allowed me to let go of something; I am not sure what, perhaps helplessness. I am glad to leave behind the shell that protected me from hurt and from meaningful contact.

Dream: *I lived in a transparent tube with others. We were safe from the enemy because our tube was impervious. I saw some men outside getting close to our tube. One got in a bulldozer and came at us really fast. I laughed, because I knew that our shell was made out of a magic material. He came right through the wall. I was electrified with fright! I broke into the opposite wall to hide in the duct work. But I knew our safety was gone. The wall had protected me all my life and now it had been breached.*

Soul Tree

Dream: *There were several books on a table. I wanted to have one that I thought of as being meant for me. But they were trying to get me to take a different one. I said I didn't want it because it has all of the answers in it already. I need to find my own answers.*

The Soul Tree is a magical tree whose leaves and fruit are the source of all the souls in the universe. It grows in the heart of the garden of origin. *A Memory of What We Agreed to Forget* also had an apple tree on the woman's chest. Now the tree has become three–dimensional, growing out of her heart. The woman has also become three–dimensional. The apple in her hand represents her individual soul.

Both the painting and dream speak to me of the quest for my unique nature. We are all part of the same tree, only the journey reveals to us if we are root, leaf, blossom, or fruit. Perhaps a metamorphosis occurs as the voyage continues. If that were to be the case, I imagine you could start life as a seed and end as a root.

Whole at Heart

Dr. W. and I were discussing how well things were going in the therapy process. I said that I felt I was nearly through taking the pieces of my life apart to examine them. Now I could begin to put them together again. He said, "Yes, and now it will be like a stained glass window that is much stronger than one ridged pane of glass." As he said that, I knew I had to paint the image, one of wholeness made up of many parts. The feminine and masculine symbols, firmly in my hold, promise compassion and purpose for the journey.

I asked my dream self to send me a sign if I had completed my work. As I ponder the words, interpretation, and translation, I see that I have examined my source. Now it is time to transform its power over me into personal strength.

Dream: *There was a classroom situation: blackboard, people in chairs, maybe someone at the front of the room. I was sitting in one of the chairs. I realized that I had been missing the point. I had thought of it like song interpretation, but it is really more like language translation. I must look deeper for he meaning.*

Dream: *I was having an opening at Dr. W.'s office. His wife wasn't too sure this was appropriate. But he said artists do these things from time to time—it's part of the process. I became doubtful and started to leave. The whole place was dark. I hadn't actually seen anyone yet. The only light was the patch from outside the front door. As I headed toward it, I bumped into Dr. W. He recognized me even in the dark. He said, "There you are! Have a seat." He sat, too. He said, "If I had to choose between $500,000 or both, I'd take both."*

Then the entertainment began. Dr. W., his dad, and Dick put on the farce. They were the Three Musketeers. Dr. W. was very funny. They were all fencing on the balcony.

It is my turn to tell a story. I say I don't know where to start. Several young women posed in front of me, saying "Did it start like this? Like this?" Exasperated, I waved them away. I will tell the story myself. I stand and wave my left arm. A window appears into the past. It is a view of Dr. W. and me in his office. He is meditating cross-legged on a cushion. I am standing behind him wearing a cloak of night. All is silent, but I know that I am telling him tales. It reminds me of the 1,001 Nights. He turns and whirls a silver chain toward my face. It has stars and moons on it. The chain keeps it from hitting me. He whirls it around and around.

Suddenly we are back in the "now," and I am clothed only in silver jewelry. Heavy coils of silver with designs in it wrap up my legs and arms, around my body and breasts. I am alone dancing. As I dance, my arms and legs sometimes reach out and sweep the sky. At other times I am still in the dark room. At one point my foot sweeps back a drapery to reveal a huge case of books.

I feel wonderful! Light—free—powerful. Then I think—stoned! Oh no! I'm stoned. That's against all the rules. This isn't real at all. I woke up. As I woke I realized that I wasn't stoned but dreaming. It was real after all.

A Dream of Unity: All for One and One for All

In this significant dream the men are not only positive figures, but they are playful and cast as protectors. I realized that it was important to bring these characters into the conscious world by painting the dream, making their magical healing powers a permanent part of my life.

That Dr. W. knows me even in the dark indicates that I believe he sees my elemental self. The masculine triad of mentor, father, and companion/lover combine to create a whole and healthy animus. The Three Musketeers are protectors of the queen, so I feel very safe to proceed with my story. As I do my Life Dance, I feel powerfully connected, like Wonder Woman. I am cloaked in mystery, capable of reaching the heights and revealing wisdom. What a wonderful dream full of promise and the power of unity. I especially like the affirmation that this is no drug–induced delirium, but a true life dream.

5. Accepting the Cure

The Moment of Loss

Dream: *There were three women. They were wearing blouses or dresses made out of material that had similar patterns but different colors. I knew they were one woman, but they didn't.*

It has become important to face my traumas as completely as possible in the hope that they will lose their power over me. With this image I am, once again, connecting with the feelings experienced during the gang rape. *The Moment of Loss* shows the devastation of my inner unity as a result of that violation. Rage, pain, and oblivion are personified in this image.

I have become aware of three aspects of my self who are trying to reunite. They appear in many ways. The child without a childhood, the wife whose fear left her childless, and the woman who emerges from them are all of the same body. We are told that to truly experience the wonder of the world we must become as a child. That is the promise of maturity, growing past fear and into wonder again, as a whole person.

Daddy Enraged

Dr. W. guided me through role playing with my three aspects of self. I simply couldn't take the role of my angry self. So when I got home, I decided to let her paint again. For the first time, I painted a "child view" image in a life-size scale. I have been going through yet another spiral of emotion centered around my father. I am seeing how very wrong it was, and is, for anyone to be beaten. No one has the right to beat others, especially helpless children.

Like the girl in the dream, I have found a way around the taboo on telling. But I also have to be alert to ways that I try to shoot myself down by demeaning my efforts.

Dream: *The children had a secret, and someone was shooting them one by one, so they wouldn't tell. A high-powered rifle was used, so that death took them unaware. A teenage girl, who couldn't speak, wrote music to tell the secret. Just as she was conducting the symphony to play the piece, she was shot. I had the sense of both doing the shooting and being shot.*

The Unwilling Sacrifice

Dream: *There were many gathered for the funeral of two Indians. The painted faces of the Indians were cut off and put on a platter. One was an adult and one a child. It was my job to cut the faces up with a hatchet and throw bits on the mourners. Then I left to hide in a diorama of a European living room, circa 1939-40. I thought perhaps there would be a way to enter the real world at that point. Then I thought that since I was a Jew, it wouldn't be such a great idea.*

Dr. W. had been talking about the concept of service and of the value of being a willing sacrifice. I sacrifice willingly by sharing my life experiences. As a child, however, I was not a willing participant in those experiences. It is the unwilling child who painted this picture, complete with the avenging angel who comes in answer to her prayers.

My original selves, child and adult, are the sacrifice. They face the world in pieces, willingly sacrificed by my hand. A new sense of self may enter the world by following the courageous example of Charlotte Salomon in the book, *Charlotte: Life or Theater?*, who was Jewish, although I am not. I feel ambivalent, being brave means facing danger. Dr. W. recommended Victor Frankl's *Man's Search for Meaning*, a deep and moving view of life in the death camps where the soul's survival depended upon finding a purpose in suffering and even in death. I must seek my own guiding truth.

The Healing Dream

I picked out my first car today. I have decided to learn to drive. It is a decision that seems to have appeared "out of the blue," as though some long forgotten part of me has awakened.

This dream tells me life is not a spectator activity. I need to live as though my very soul depends on my actions. Years ago I had a dream in which Dick was driving and I was beside him. We were going up a mountain, when suddenly I found myself at the side of the road as he continued upward. A booming voice on the sound track said, "You can't get to heaven if you don't drive the car." Driving has become a metaphor for taking responsibility for my life.

Dream: I had unclear dreams about driving. Also, there was a man who sacrificed his life so others could live. They all applauded him. He was disappointed in their applause. It showed that they missed the point. This was more than a performance. Their souls were at stake.

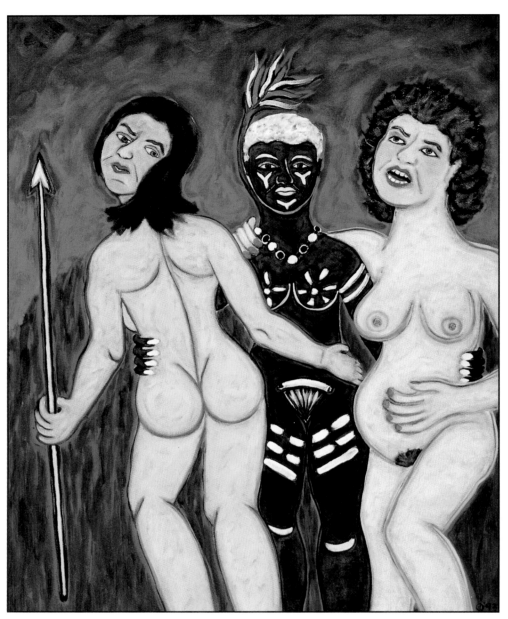

Protector, Healer, Creator

Dream: *There was a large meeting of the minds. They were to solve the world's greatest problem. I left the main auditorium going into a vast hallway. It appeared empty. I decided I needed a new perspective. Then I saw people, in many colors, with painted faces. Though they spoke in another language I knew that they had discovered the secret. I asked them to tell me. They said no, no—as though I wouldn't be able to understand, not being of their culture. But I said, "Please try me." One, more willing to trust me than the rest, held his hand up and cried out, "Be who you really are!" There was silence for a moment. Suddenly another ran up to him and matched his hand to the other crying, "Be who you really are." Then all the people were matching hands and crying out. I reached my hand out to several people but they went on by. I reached out to a little girl, but we had both put out our right hands instead of a right and a left. She said, "I can only do it with this hand." It was important to me that we greet one another.*

This dream had a powerful effect on me. Approaching the canvas, I asked the question, "Who am I, really?" I was given the true names of my three most often seen aspects, standing together as one.

The matching of opposite hands seems an important aspect of this dream. We contain many opposites within us. Each of these three aspects contain their opposites as well. The Protector might go on the attack. The Creator is known to destroy. And the Healer may decide that illness is the surest route to wholeness. They symbolize the mystery of Many and One.

Guardians of the Soul

In looking at the dreamer in *The Healing Dream*, I decided that she needed help to wake from her 40-year sleep. So I sent the Protector, Healer, and Creator into her tomb to attend her.

When I view life as a game, I visualize the ultimate goal as the discovery of one's true self. This game of hide-and-seek is played with the gods. Sometimes the gods challenge us with trials, sometimes they whisper clues in our dreams. They tell us to use all of our powers. They say they are allies rather than adversaries.

Dream: *We came to play with the gods, and I only have a child's weapons.*

Lessons at My Mother's Knee

Dream: I was playing cards with my folks. The cards were family photos. I didn't have any good cards, but Mom laid down some winning pairs. She thought she had won until Dad said, "You forgot the Bonus Rule," as he laid down three sets of three cards each. They were all photos of him in power suits. Mom got angry. She said, "How can he win when I have this on the wall for all to see?" "This" was a bloody bunch of rags nailed to the wall among the family photos. It was all that was left of the sheets on which she had borne her children. Proof of her martyrdom. She knew she had lost and the injustice of it stung her.

For years I sought my mother's love and protection but was left alone and vulnerable. In this exploration of the mother/daughter relationship, I have provided images of nurturing, giving to myself, now, what I needed then. Perhaps it will work like magic back through the years. Through my painting I not only explore the past, but hope to redefine it.

This dream displays the anger, resentfulness, and martyrdom that I saw in my mother. I undoubtedly carry all of these feelings within myself as well. The bloody rags on my wall have to do with rape rather than child-bearing and my feelings are more deeply hidden. I think the dream is reminding me that we are not so very different.

I Am My Parent's Child

In talking over last night's dream with Dr. W., he suggested that I repeat, "I am my parent's child," over and over as a way of acceptance. I repeated that mantra while doing this painting. We are of the same tree, but I must find my own truth and beauty in the stream of life.

I project on my mother the role of condemning me as a traitor. In spite of all the exhibits of my artwork and talking openly about the past, there is a part of me—a judgmental mother figure—who scorns my activities. My mother may have also scorned my paintings, but I think the dream is more concerned with my inner life than with my actual relationship with my mother.

Dream: *I went to visit my parents in California. I was struck by the fact that they were always moving and not welcome anywhere. My feeling was, not only were they unwanted by their children, but by each other as well. Impulsively, I invited mom to come and visit us. As I woke up, I thought, oh no, I will have to hide all of my paintings, and even then she will find out that I told. I have betrayed my ancestors.*

Don't Touch Me! I'm Alive

Dream: *We are too polite to notice or speak of it. How could we ignore the destruction of that child? That would be like saying she doesn't exist. If she doesn't exist, neither do we. If we don't exist, there is no need to be so polite.*

When speaking about the gang rape in this week's session, I said that I was laid on the bed like a thing with no life. In this image I am no longer an anonymous, unfeeling stick figure. I am alive, and resisting.

Raging Against Futile Prayers

When I was 13, I began going to church twice on Sunday and once in the middle of the week. I prayed and prayed for relief from my pain and rage. I didn't find it. As a result of my confession when I was "saved," my tormentor was kept away from me for a while. No one ever spoke of it beyond a chance remark 30 years later. But the fact remained that I was the same damaged person. My sins weren't washed away. Even as the minister dipped me in the water I feared his eyes on my body beneath the wet gown. His illicit touch was expected with dread, because he was a man and I was already tainted. I was surprised when it didn't happen. My impure thoughts told me that the cross I prayed at was only wood, there was no Savior for such as I.

A Child with a Few Illusions Left

Dream: *It would be easier to find a pimple on a snake's butt than it would be to discover the truth.*

I was talking about the child I was before the worst things happened. Dr. W. encouraged me to connect with her. So I have been looking at old photos.

There were many taboo subjects when I was young. Most of those taboos persist today. Outright lies were the norm, as well. Who broke the lamp? Let the dog loose? Ate the leftovers? Went joyriding in the car? These were questions asked and lied about. Who beat up mother? Raped Jane? Gambled the rent on a horse? These were questions that weren't open to discussion. The truth becomes fluid. Each of us carries our own portion of a puzzle too huge to assemble.

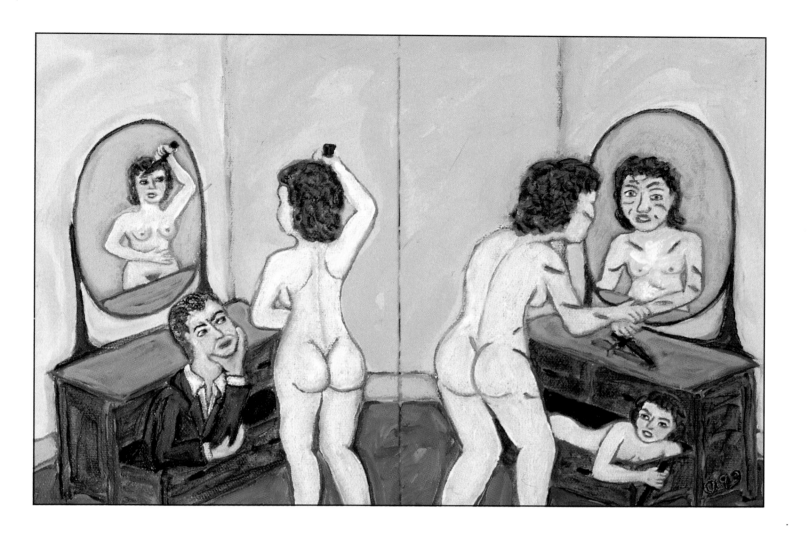

Witness to the Wounds

Dr. W., having helped to resurrect the remains of the past, now acts as witness to the story of the wounds. Opening the wounds allows them to form scars on the outside, a sign of healing. Each symbolic cut is a secret told, poison released. As in homeopathy, the distilled essence of the illness becomes the antidote. Health returns by tracing the path of the illness back to the memory of wholeness contained in each body cell.

On the surface, these years of therapy have been about dealing with the childhood traumas of rape and incest (broiling the hot dogs!) On a deeper level the quest has been to become spiritually whole (transforming rocks into silver knives). In reality, the taxman would allow the expense of addressing psychological problems caused by rape and childhood trauma. Money spent on reviving the connections between body and spirit, however, wouldn't make it past the scrutiny of the I.R.S. I have an inner taxman who has been questioning me about the continued expense of therapy now that the hot dogs have been broiled. The dream indicates that was just a preliminary step, not my final mission.

Dream: *Dr. W. and I were melting rocks in a big outdoor cooker. It looked like a dresser. We cast the rocks into beautiful sets of silver knives. The handles were all engraved with a shiny swirling design. When the taxman came to investigate, we fooled him into thinking we were just broiling hot dogs.*

The Magician Reveals All

Dream: *Some people were being held prisoner. It was hot and sunny. It was suggested that we all take off our clothes and go swimming. We started to undress—then stopped. We wondered how we would be able to tell who was the guard and who the prisoner if we had no clothes.*

A therapist can act as a magic mirror, revealing what is contained in one's self. So as I look at the glass, I may see his clothes but not him. I see the combination of light and dark, which is me. The magician gains this power by virtue of his training, and because the client grants it through a willingness to participate.

In a painting it is not unusual for Dr. W. to have clothes when I do not. His suit is a symbol of his role, he keeps his self hidden. It is my job to reveal. At a symbolic or archetypal level, where most of the action occurs, there are few clothes to obscure one's meaning. The dream reminds me that we are both prisoners to our role, unknowable to one another outside of our theater, where he is the director and I am the play.

Dr. W.

I often envision the therapy process as graduate school, with myself as the course of study. Dr. W. has been a guide, listener, advisor, commentator, catalyst, and source of empowering energy. He is also a great storyteller, using folk tales, myth, Eastern and Western history, and religion, along with jokes from the junior high school set, to illuminate his observations. The therapy is focused on me, the client, but with this portrait I hoped to penetrate the mirror to see the man who holds it.

In dreaming of my graduation, I find that though I still have much to learn, I now have a firm foundation and an incisive tool to work with. Luckily, I was in Wyoming when I had this dream, a great place to be when looking for a knife. This gift from my dream self has a round wooden handle with silver inlays, a silver blade, and a leather sheath. The knife is no longer a threat to me, but a symbol of self–mastery.

Dream: *I had been taking classes to bring myself up to a level where I could begin my postgraduate studies. I graduated from these studies and bought myself a gift as a symbol of what I'd learned and as a tool for further studies. It was also a reward. It was a knife.*

6. Soul Journey

Alchemist's Dream

Dream: *I was collecting beautiful stones and metals. I had to pay for each one. I soon ran out of coins and had to choose older stones and pieces of metal to exchange for the new ones. It was OK to give up the coins but hard to part with the others, because of their beauty or charm.*

The heat of the sun, the silence of the desert, and the cool of the ocean at night combine to create an impression of purification and timelessness. Water has come to the wasteland and with it the promise of rejuvenation. The water of life represents the source of all things, the cosmic womb. It is a symbol of physical, emotional, and spiritual cleansing.

The lovely bits of metal and smooth stones we collect along life's shore become symbols of our growing soul. Their messages grow in us as we hold and polish them. Sometimes we grow enchanted by the glitter without considering the price to be paid. Money is a trifling matter but soul growth requires letting go of old ways of being. Like the alchemist, we must be willing to burn away the unworthy self to find the nobility and beauty hidden within. My fear is that beneath the coals in the fire pit, I will find nothing of value.

Transformation by the Slime Pits

Having recently read Nikos Kazantzakis' *Saviors of God*, I was deeply affected by his vision of the human ascent from the primordial essence. Human is my word choice; he is concerned solely with man. His only reference to women is that they bear their male children well. Looking past that failing, it is a passionate vision of the human spirit, merging with the Abyss, struggling from the Abyss, transcending the Abyss.

I know that I, too, have been transformed by the slime pits. Now my mission is to run toward the light and glow with its reflection. The horse, a potent creative symbol, is my companion. Strength and the ability to reflect are my gifts from the Abyss. Pegasus sprang from the severed head of the Medusa, beauty and grace from ugliness and death.

Dream: *There was a white horse. It was magic. It had laid down in a radioactive slime pit and had a translucent glow—white—like a glow-in-the-dark cross. It could run faster than any other being. I ran in front of it.*

Nature's Child

I realized that I hadn't checked in with my child self lately. So I asked her to do a painting and tell me how she is feeling. It is important that she is still a part of me and has, also, evolved. She is not stuck in the misery I found her in five years ago. Here she looks like the child of nature who, years ago, discovered the magical pool by the lake. Now she knows the dark side of nature, as well as her own dark side; knowledge leading out of the slime pit toward a luminous world.

Me and My Shadow, Together Again

The wolf or dog has served as my symbol of the inner and outer beast. My relationship to this figure has changed over the past five years from one of terrified revulsion to one of active willingness to learn from this fierce inner resource.

The dream suggests I have garnered qualities through my association with Dr. W. to create a more decorous beast. Once disdained, this beast now has obvious good breeding. The elegance of a boxer, with a touch of bulldog for tenacity, is combined with civilized behavior and intelligence.

Dream: *Dr. W.'s wife and family had come to visit, perhaps to see the yard. They also brought their dog, a boxer with just a touch of bulldog in him. I poured apricot juice in the glasses for her and the children. They were all aloof but the dog was interested in everything, so I left them and went with the dog to investigate. We went upstairs to the balcony. There was a nice old overstuffed chair, and I patted the seat to indicate he was welcome to sit there. He was surprised and pleased that I would allow him on the furniture. He sat upright in the chair and expressed his pleasure by speaking with me at great length about his observations of the world. I was momentarily surprised that he could talk and then pleased that he trusted me. Later I went back and got the bottle of apricot juice and refilled the glasses.*

The Juggler Holds Trumps

In the therapy process, feelings toward parents, siblings, and partners are often transferred to the therapist. As the client, I may project unwel–come aspects of myself to the therapist as well. It appears that Dr. W. holds all the cards but, on looking closer, he is depicted as being diminished by that power, since his head is smaller than those he juggles. This makes sense as, in reality, I can never know him as a person outside of the context of therapy. Like the juggler or jester, Dr. W. uses wit and droll humor to reveal unpleasant truths. This is the child's painting, she now holds both comfort and protection. Dr. W. has a print on his wall of a gateway. In its place I have painted *Rape*, the image that was the gateway leading into this healing body of work, just as the original rape was the gateway to a world of pain and confusion.

Mystery of Opposites

When I put Dr. W. in the center of this painting, it was my adult self responding to the issue of transference, which can be the result of either positive or negative feelings being shifted to the therapist. I am most aware of negative transference. The image is like a self–portrait, except that he stands in my place and carries my negative aura for me. He has created a safe, neutral screen on which I can project my emotions, making them visible. Then he can walk out from behind the screen and we can talk about the mystery of the opposing forces as they interact on the human level. It is a powerful and mysterious process that requires mutual goodwill and commitment. Awareness grows as I become conscious of how emotional responses learned in childhood continue to dictate my actions in adult life.

Pandora's Box

Dream: *It was time to find what was hidden away. Much of it was left in some old trunks in a house we had lived in many years ago. They were left unlocked so that no one would guess their value. Some thought we should have a public ceremony—a coming-of-age party with all the old tales. I agreed that the tales were necessary but insisted that I didn't know them. I preferred a private setting in the hills for the ceremony, around a campfire, and perhaps have a public event later after we had opened all the trunks and assembled the whole. The fairy tales, myths, and the saga could all be told again. The child was running around, excited that the time had come in her lifetime. I was enlivened by the decision, too, but was aware that there was much work to be done. What is the "whole" after all? And the man kept referring to me as the one to tell the tales. I didn't know them—maybe they are in the trunks too.*

Once upon a time, long, long ago, things happened that changed my life forever. I didn't want to accept those events and feelings so, instinctively, I created parts of my self to carry those events. In time these aspects of self were no longer actively needed. They were packed away, hidden in an old trunk, until I could gain the will and the strength to be whole again.

I have been opening trunks for five years. Besides old memories, I have found pain and confusion, as well as vitality, determination, even compassion. The need for ceremony mentioned in the dream suggests that the next trunks may contain holy objects, dedicated to service. My duty, it appears, is to tell the tales of spiritual renewal, even though I feel reluctant and ill prepared.

Memory, Meditation, and Song

The three primary aspects of my self revealed to me through this visual journey have been transformed by time and the process of surrender, dedication, and blessing.

So often, in the theater of my dreams, the image of cleaning or doing laundry becomes a metaphor for therapy. Water, in this case, represents the dark and mysterious, the unconscious. The dirt becomes fluid, the water murky. Strange monsters are let loose. In the painting I am harvesting the monsters of my memories, the rapists. I extract all of the emotional energy of that experience so that I am no longer controlled by those emotions. In the dream, and in the image, I find my center. Rather than becoming the monster, I transform my fear of the dragon into a song inspired by its fierceness and dedicated to my own wild power.

Dream: *I entered a theater where the box seats were beds. A janitor came to clean up. I was concerned that no water touch my bed or me. He threw a wet rag on my bed. I freaked out. Some water got on me. It had weird life in it. Someone said you are changing already— growing scales and wings. I panicked. Then I caught myself. Be calm, you can handle this. I began to sing the first song that came to my head. When the song was done, I made up a new one. The singing saved me. I quit mutating, stabilized. I could survive.*

Portal to the Infinite

I decided to paint a mandala, a symbolic diagram, or mystical map, of the cosmos and of the human soul. A mandala functions as a meditative device allowing one to focus on the spiritual realm. I stand on the threshold of timelessness surrounded by the elemental opposites. Simply said, I am aware of the forces that shape my life, yet I am still separate from these forces. I sense a need to integrate their meaning, beyond the intellectual, into my life.

The dream reminds me that it is difficult to see trials clearly when caught in the midst of them. I have scaled the mountain and have only to cross the portal to be safely home from my journey. But I am lost, in doubt, and unable to see the final step. The anger, frustration and laughter that I ascribe to Dr. W. in the dream probably come from my inner taxman who wants me "to find myself" and be done with this spirit quest.

Dream: *I was with Dick on a high, barren mountain. I was trying to lead us to a path to descend, but the trail kept disintegrating beneath me. It was scary and dangerous. We had looked down from the mountain earlier and saw Dr. W. drive up and park. He was waiting for us. So I decided that I had better go back to the area where he was to tell him not to wait because we couldn't find our way down. He was upset, angry even, at us for taking so long. When I explained that we couldn't find our way off the mountain, he looked at my feet, then his feet and began laughing. At that point our mountain was only one foot high. We only had to step off the curb.*

Sailing to Where the Dreams Are Kept

I am the fisherwoman sailing into the sunset for night fishing. I will cast my nets on the sea of the unconscious. When I began this journey in 1990, I hadn't recorded a dream in the previous seven years. After several months of psychotherapy, I began to remember my dreams. I recorded 147 in that first year, 90 in the second, 55 in the third and 50 more in the last four years. In the initial stages of therapy my nights were fully as active as my days. The connection to my dream self, spirit self, was deep and full. Now I am in calmer waters.

This dream, from early 1990, describes a place where dreams are kept. It has a deep pool of water; other dreams might have a stream or flooded roads. Deep water contains secrets, still water reflects images back to us, moving water can sweep us away or carry us toward our destination. Water represents the powers of the unconscious, the source of dreams.

Dream: *I was with a group of people in a dark place. It was like a painting on black velvet. There was a deep pool. Bits of our souls were reflected back at us on the pool like mosaics. There was a child who would disappear when someone spoke to her. The child would, like magic, go inside a ball. Sometimes she would go down into a second ball, and only a bit of her cloak would remain visible at the hole she disappeared through. We were supposed to tell stories. I was going to tell about a woman who was lying on a couch. She was tired. I said my story wouldn't be too exciting. I would tell only how she smiled briefly, then went to sleep.*

The Gift

Dream: *Dr. W. had a special gift for me. I was two girls and I was pleased with him that he could give it to me and see both my body and soul selves at once. The gift was a symbol of the two of me meeting each other. One was sitting on a cube, reaching upwards, all was enclosed within a glass ball, the mundane world. The soul self was on top of the ball but had put her arm inside to touch the hand of her bodily self, thereby gifting her with animation. Dr. W. said "Now that you have this gift you must leave our session by 4:15, you can't linger to play with the other children anymore." I took that to mean that I was becoming a grown-up.*

The Gift speaks of aspects of my self interacting through layers—body to soul—soul to body. As the painting took shape, my spiritual self appeared in her own dimension. She acts as a guiding presence. The gift refers to the ability to interact with the past, thereby redeeming it, creating new possibilities for the future.

This dream resonates of the previous dream, from 1990, of the child who hides in the magic ball. The power of the story has released her from the need to remain hidden. Periodically my dreams suggest that it is time for me to graduate, move on, grow up. In fact, two sessions ago, Dr. W. And I had agreed to meet only three more times. However, having so thoroughly taken my life apart to examine each piece, I want to be equally exacting in its reconstruction. The road to emotional well–being includes curves, bumps, and detours. Even though I have at last found the road, I still want to keep my guide. I will continue to see Dr. W. for another 30 sessions in the next two years.

I Was Blind but Now I See

Looking at the metaphor of the ball within the ball, within the ball, helps me to see myself in terms of time as well as body, soul, and spirit; or the persona, animus, and archetypal aspects of self. The world is a strangely magical place, where a line can become a dot and a visible dot contains millions of invisible dots. As a child, for the most part, I was blind to the future and blind to the world outside of my immediate circle. Now I can see my past and my present more fully, with a view into the future, as well. The future is revealed, not as a vision in a crystal ball, but by an awareness of the interrelatedness of past, present, and future events.

Dance of the Sacred Heart

This painting is a visual summation of the process of therapy. One shares with a trained observer and guide the many aspects of the self. In examining the mundane, we see the symbolic that leads us into the arche-typal realm. The figures in the foreground first appeared in my work six years ago in the painting titled, *Me, Myself and I*. They have been my interior guides, acting out the parts in the drama to make the mysterious knowable. In such a drama, a life dance, even the smallest person can gain the strength of an elephant by facing the inner beast. The lion is put through his paces, seemingly controlled by the lion tamer, but in the end she has to have the courage to bow to him, to offer her head to the King should he choose to take it. The clever jester shares the spotlight with the outright clown. Strength, courage, and humor are all needed to perform in the dance. It brings together the forces of dark and light to reveal the drama of life in all of its complexity. The meaning is discovered while the sacred heart beats its time for the dance.

7. Celebration

Transformed by Time

Until now the symbolism of the balloons has evaded me, but as
I painted this mural–size canvas, their meaning became clear. They repre–
sent the fragmented self, the child who became lost in pain, anger, and the
yearning for oblivion. The persona had carried them into adulthood, but
kept them outside of her consciousness, on a long tether. Through the
creative act they have become visible and gained vitality. In coming to
know them, I have been released from the control they held without my
knowledge. Because of all that I have learned from them, I have willingly
given my promise to serve in the name of the child. The metamorphosis of
the fractured childhood self to a whole adult is brought about, through
time, by a series of transforming experiences. Some are as simple as grow–
ing flowers for 20 years, some depend on the love of others or on the
mantra of creativity. All depend on grace.

Dangerous Waters

The pearl, a symbol of
wisdom, owes its existence to
the flaw at its heart, the speck
of grit around which the
layers of pearl essence form.
The metamorphosis takes
many years in deep, dark,
dangerous waters, symbolic
of the unconscious. The
search for this particle of
true grit becomes the
search for one's self.

A Piece of the Infinite

Just as the yin is stagnant
without the speck of yang
within it, finite existence is
animated by the infinite and
the infinite given life in the
finite. In the depths of my
psyche, I have discovered the
piece of the Infinite Being that
renews my life, the point of
light hidden in the darkness.
Beneath the layers of shame,
anger, pain, and cynicism, as
well as the layers of opposing
feelings that cloak those layers,
there lies a bit of truth. A truth
I accepted in my head years
ago, but now I see with my
heart. Since all of the life force
is divine, I myself am worthy.

Anima/Animus

While going through the trunks, I have been able to discard much that was no longer relevant, making room for more appropriate symbols through which the world may be viewed. The inner masculine no longer carries the aspect of the beast. He is intelligent, self–assured, organized, and fun–loving. The beast has its own corner in my soul, but now, rather than running wild as it once did, it serves as a guard dog. My refurbished animus reflects qualities seen in Dick, Dr. W., my favorite brothers, and friends, but he is uniquely mine.

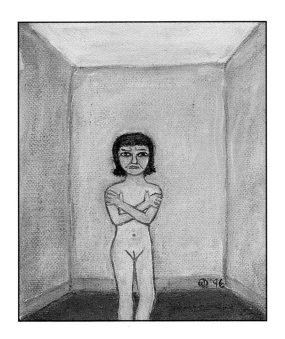

Locked in Fear

In pondering my goals, "Take Charge" popped into my head. Perhaps once a year for the past five years, Dr. W. has mentioned "Take Charge," an organization that teaches full force self-defense. He had attended a graduation and was so impressed that he later took part in a weekend workshop for therapists. He wished to know more, in case he decided to recommend the experience to a client. I asked my child self how she felt about her defense capabilities. This painting was her reply. So I called them. They have one opening left for the class beginning in two weeks. There are five sessions of six hours each, all within a two–week period of time. It will be a challenging way to celebrate my 54th birthday.

Turning the Tables

I don't feel threatened in my world today. The decision to "Take Charge" is a gift I am giving to my child self. I want her to feel safe and powerful. She exhibits confidence and good form in this image painted toward the end of the course. There were 14 women in the class. All of us knew what it was to be assaulted and have no means of defense. Some were totally panicked to be touched by a man. We had two courageous and compassionate men, highly athletic instructors, who played the part of assailants. They were well–padded. We learned to deliver full force blows, placed in such a way as to put them out of action. We had a marvelous female instructor right beside us, coaching and encouraging every step of the way. When panic stopped us, she helped turn that terror into action—full force self-defense. Three past graduates completed the instructional team. They gave support and kept us moving. With their skills and each woman's commitment, the class bonded as a group in the first session. I was the oldest by 15 years and not in the best of shape. Although we each had handicaps to overcome or work within, there was never any doubt that we would all emerge triumphant.

Magic Carpet Dream

I suddenly feel the desire to celebrate treasured memories, the magic moments of childhood that made my life worth living. I loved being in trees, viewing the world from high above. Trees were not only a place to hide, they were a place to dream.

In the dream, we asked simultaneously about the book, making me think there must be such a book and that I should read it. After a search, I found it. First published in 1884, *Flatland* is a narrative of a two–dimensional world, a presentation of geometrical concepts and a barbed satire of the hierarchical world of the Victorians. It gave me a renewed sense of the value of challenging a given perspective of the world. I have focused on the deep pain of my past and have found that pain is the heart of the pearl. My life history hasn't changed—the pain is still there, but my perspective has changed. I have discovered that, indeed, the worst in me is the best in me.

Dream: *Dick and I were in the car going through a flood. We had to pull off the road several times for emergency vehicles. The last time I saw rescuers who had just brought in a rock climber. He had gone up beyond his ability to return. He came to talk to me. I said I could imagine myself in that same position. But, I said I thought it was better to have gone too high than to never have left the flatlands. Then we both said at once, "Have you read Flatland?"*

Garden Sanctuary

My love of gardening originally grew out of the discovery that no one ever bothered me when I was weeding. It was a safe haven. I learned to delight in the unfolding of life, the taste of fresh-picked food and the beauty of flowers. Today my yard is a mix of blossoms and art. It is my sanctuary, but it is also a magic moment shared. Many people return year after year, looking for changes in the yard, and bringing new friends along to share in the magic. If they see me weeding in the yard, they rarely speak to me. No one wants to interrupt a weeder.

My Momma Used to Call Me Her Water Baby

The magic of this moment was captured on film 50 years ago. The color has faded, the photo is cracked and torn, but I treasure it. Oh, how I loved the water! I could swim the length of the big pool the summer I was 3 1/2. The pool was 10 blocks away. I spent the whole summer there and the next two as well. It was especially nice on the weekends, when Momma could come. She took my picture and I was happy. I felt special.

Dream: *I was a visitor of some sort in a run-down house and needed to stay the night. I could sense that FEAR had become lodged in the house. When they offered me the roll-out bed, the woman said I might prefer the floor because FEAR had taken up residence in this bed. The woman was very big and aggressive, built like Venus of Lespugue (24,000 B.C.). She had the aspect of the Devouring Mother. The man in the house was nurturing. Later I went out on the back porch, and FEAR was out there. I asked him if he would like a ride back into town (since he had lost his body, so to speak). He said "No, I have two more years of work in this house." When the man and I were ready to leave in the morning, it was still dark and stormy, with thunder and lightening. I said perhaps it is not safe to even drive in this storm. He said, no, it is always like this when we leave. FEAR hates to be left behind, especially to be left with that woman.*

Painful Parting

While calling to mind happy magical moments, this image emerged. It is also a memory holding great power, but it comes from the dark side. When I was 4 years old, my mother left me with the husband of her best friend. He was to baby–sit his two daughters and me, while the women went to pick blueberries. During nap time he molested me. As Momma and I walked home later, she knelt down on the sidewalk and asked me if he had touched me. Even at 4 years old, I thought, "If she had reason to ask that question, why did she leave me there?" He was prosecuted and spent the next five years in prison. Forty years later I finally asked what made her ask that question. She said that she was suspicious, because he had been previously convicted of child molestation. I couldn't bring myself to ask why she had left me there. This image refers to that time and all of the subsequent times she left me in danger.

In the fear, I leave FEAR behind; he is no longer embodied in me. He still lives in the rundown house where I used to stay. My masculine self and I have moved on. FEAR has unfinished business with the aspect of my self symbolized by the Devouring Mother. She is ancient and more powerful than FEAR. Throughout this journey, I have been aware of a great reluctance to investigate feelings about Mother—earthly or archetypal. In paintings, my mother is usually seen wringing her hands or leaving. In this image, for the first time, there is a suggestion that she might be distressed to leave me. The lightening speaks of a higher power at work, her fate and mine, which decreed the paths we were to take.

Puss and I in the Studio

After seven years of exploring my past through painting, writing, and dreams, I am delighted with this image. It is so firmly in the here and now. Here, in the studio with my companion on the journey, Puss. She came to me in the guise of an alley cat. As we have traveled together she has transformed into a princess. But like me, she hasn't forgotten her origins. She retains the knowledge and skills of an alley cat, and can defend and provide for herself. Appropriately, the cat was honored as the sacred animal of the goddess Bast, the protectress of home, mother, and children.

She Is Stronger Than She Looks

This well-grounded, earnest child is now better able to bear the weight of the long body. Her strength and determination allowed me to survive to adulthood. As an adult, I have been able to seek the necessary help to heal her pain and fragmentation. The girl who was split apart by trauma has been unified by self-knowledge. As a further step toward wholeness, I gave her the gift of "Take Charge." That training in self-defense has given her bone-deep knowledge that she can defend herself. She easily supports the long-distance swimmer, the young adult self who carried me from the dangerous waters of childhood to the shores of maturity. It was the young woman who discovered the valley that has become my home and the man who shares it with me. At the same time, visual expression was given to me as a tool of self-discovery. Through the labors of these younger selves, the mature self has the opportunity to fulfill her potential, to validate the years devoted to artistic development, and to redeem the child's pain.

Mother Sky Daughter Earth

Dream: *I was giving birth to a kitten but she was trying to return to my womb. I was trying to wake up to get Dick's help . . . which made me think I might be dreaming. Then I believed it was real and tried to get Dick's help again.*

Daughter Earth is born of Mother Sky. The rhythmic interplay of opposites creates the pulse that has quickened her heart. Although she has the spirit of a celestial being, she is bound to the mundane world and is destined to forget her source. That is the nature of life under the influence of gravity. Mother Sky sends storms to nurture her daughter's soul, just as the daughter's tears nourish the seed she has found and cultivated in the wasteland. The seed symbolizes the potential for transformation through evolution, an evolution of awareness. We have the possibility of knowing the source and effects of our actions and transmuting our predispositions with that knowledge. The seed is the memory of what we agreed to forget. It is the secret of life, the knowledge of good and evil, and the Mystery of the Rose as it emerges from dirt and manure.

The struggle between the urgency to give birth and the desire to return to The Mother speaks to me of a paradoxical drive for growth, combined with the fear of commitment. The nebulous border separating reality and dream seems to question whether the psychic world is real. Even though there is no physical birth, there is a birth in psychic reality, a symbolic happening that can affect life in the mundane world. They are simultaneous and reciprocal realities.

The Analytical Study of a Mystical Phenomenon

As I approach the end of therapy, I continue to be in wonder of the process and the relationship that is so intimate and yet so distant. It seems as though the very act of Dr. W.'s careful attention, his study, fuels my growth. We talk in his space but most of the action occurs in mine. Some of the action he sees, some he infers, much remains a mystery. What hap–pens behind my eyes and in my heart does not become immediately known. He waits, watches, and shares his metaphors. Dr. W.'s observation is informed by knowledge gleaned from a lifetime of reading. The sculpture on the shelf, of the two circles meeting, signifies the union of symbolic knowing with everyday reality. In the physical world and in psychic space, my stories have been told, the drama acted out by my selves who have come to know and care for one another.

Gold has many associations—eternity, perfection, insight, knowledge, love, and heavenly light. The alchemists' attempts to turn base metal into gold were associated with the quest for purification of the soul. In the dream, Dick takes the role of my inner scoffer and says it's just paint and I made a mess. But I know better; I've been blessed, baptized with gold, bestowed with magic. It's a gift in celebration of life.

Dream: *Dick and I were going along a narrow street lined with fluted lamp posts. The man who lived there had spray-painted them gold. As I went along, I put my arm around each pole and swung around it. The gold paint was still wet. It came off all over my hand, arm, and clothes. I felt bestowed upon, but Dick thought we should go back to tell the man that I messed up his paint job. I thought it was OK, it was part of the magic.*

Dream: *I woke early, thinking I had heard a noise by the back gate. Barefoot and in my nightgown, I went downstairs to investigate. It was dawn when I went outside, using the new back door. I saw no reason for the noise but discovered it had rained hard in the night. The puddles were deep and cold as I stepped out to see the huge basalt rocks that had miraculously thrust out of the ground in the night, like mushrooms after a rain. I climbed up, stepping from one to the next as I went toward the garden. It had become a deep limitless lake. I discovered a sunken dock. It sank even more as I stepped on the boards, but I followed it to where the heart-shaped goldfish pond had been in my garden. The fish had grown to as much as three feet long and were no longer contained by the pond, but swam freely now. They were vibrant with health there, among the water lilies. The boardwalk was still beneath my feet, supporting me, even though I was up to my neck in water. I reached out to and felt kinship with the goldfish, amazed by the deep mystery surrounding us.*

The Next Dream: *Our house was now in a meadow by a lake. The forest came up to the back of the house, an old wooden structure with faded yellow paint. Dick and I were younger, 25 or 30. He was out by the shore. I was also near the water but in our old yellow van. A magic fishing ritual had just been performed and the surface of the water began to vibrate. Dick raised his arms and a five-foot-long fish rose out of the water and settled onto his hands. He set the fish gently on the shore and turned toward me. I noticed the water begin to vibrate again, with much more action, and then a long creature with scales broke the surface. I called to Dick to come away, this one is too big! He came to the van with a full-grown Dragon right behind him. I urged Dick to get in; he did. The Dragon was above us, dripping hot potent water. The Dragon settled down on top of our yellow van as though it were her egg.*

The next thing I know, Dick and I are in the attic of the old house. We are now 10 years old. I realize that we are in a huge birdcage but may come and go freely. We know that the Dragon will come soon and knock the house down. She will hook her claws around the knob on top of the golden cage and carry us away. Perhaps we are her children or her treasure. She is benevolent, but she is so powerful that we must take great care to avoid harm by her very nearness.

The Deep Mystery Surrounding Us

Seven years ago, my dream self lived in a ramshackle wreck with a junky pit full of water in the backyard. My access to the pool of unconscious knowing was blocked with toxic debris. In fear of my surroundings, I constantly rebuilt my interior walls, making them thicker, allowing less light in each day. Psychic reality is much like physical reality. I couldn't wish my house clean and my water pure. I had to clean it myself, bit by bit. Each drawer had to be gone through, each memento explained. The things I saved held great power over me and couldn't just be thrown away. But I could clean them and organize them and examine them from every angle. Although loathsome at first, each time I worked on them they held less power and I held more. Eventually I had the strength to dredge the pit. There in colors of green and black and red, I found bile and hate and rage—my rejected self. Her heroic defiance had saved me years ago, but she didn't suit my notion of worthiness, so I had thrown her in the slime pit. She has grown to prefer the water and lives there still. But the water has been purified, and she is now given the honor that is her due.

The passageways have been cleared to the unconscious psychic world, the source of dreams and paintings. I am reassured that my new back door will open to a reinvigorated dawn, where the power of the masculine will lead me to the deep and limitless waters of the feminine. The submerged bridge supports me so that I may confidently explore those depths.

The dreams and paintings that have come to me from the unconscious/unseen world have been sent as gifts. They have been fashioned from my fears and my hopes to create a map leading to a place of self-knowing—place where my fears no longer have me by the throat, because they have been allowed to tell their secrets.

Now, I feel awe, rather than fear, of the Being who lives in the deep waters of the unconscious. Her colors of green, red, and black have become laced with gold, signifying her metamorphosis from destroyer to creator. She is no longer confined, but can swim freely and even fly. The calling ritual brought her to us, and her potency transformed us. Wondrously, the once warring masculine and feminine factions within me have been reborn, twins, incubated in the golden Dragon egg. There is a promise of adventure on the journey ahead if I put my trust in the Dragon energy being offered. The dream world has sent me a final gift, a token from the Dragon. It is a symbol of love, courage, pain, and beauty, a carved wooden heart with a painted red rose, thorns along the stem. It plays the melody, "You Are My Sunshine," causing a spontaneous smile at the message that I hold in the palm of my hand.

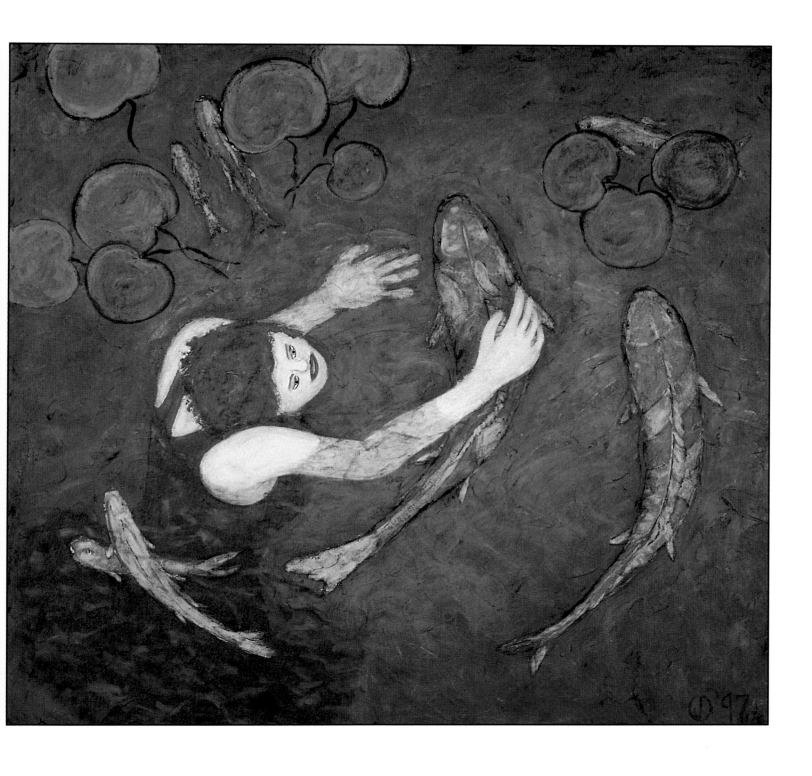

References

Abbott, E. A. (1953). *Flatland: A romance of many dimensions.* New York: Dover Publications.

Bly, R. (1988). *The little book on the human shadow.* San Francisco: Harper & Row.

Frankl, V. E. (1963). *Man's search for meaning: An introduction to logotherapy.* New York: Washington Square Press.

Freiburg, H. (1988). *The Herder symbol dictionary* (Boris Matthews, Trans.). Wilmette, IL: Chiron Publications.

Harding, M. E. (1948). *Psychic energy: Its source and transformation.* New York: Pantheon Books

Harding, M. E. (1976). *Woman's mysteries: Ancient and modern.* New York: Harper & Row.

Jung, C. G. (1933). *Modern man in search of a soul* (W. S. Dell and C. F. Baynes, Trans.). New York: Harcourt, Brace & World, Inc.

Jung, C. G. (1963). *Memories, dreams and reflections.* Aniela Jaffe (Ed.), (Richard and Clara Winston, Trans.). New York: Random House.

Jung, C. G. (1964). *Man and his symbols.* Garden City, NY: Doubleday & Co.

Kazantzakis, N. (1960). *The saviors of God: Spiritual exercises* (Kimon Friar, Trans.). New York: Simon and Schuster.

Miller, A. (1984). *Pictures of a childhood: Sixty-six watercolors and an essay* (Hildegarde and Hunter Hannum, Trans.). New York: Farrar Straus.

Miller, A. (1990). *The untouched key: Tracing childhood trauma in creativity and destructiveness* (Hildegarde and Hunter Hannum, Trans.). New York: Doubleday.

Perera, S. B. (1981). *Descent to the goddess: A way of initiation for women.* Toronto: Inner City books.

Perera, S. B. (1986). *The scapegoat complex: Toward a mythology of shadow and guilt.* Toronto: Inner City Books.

Salomon, C. (1981). *Charlotte: Life or theater?* (Leila Vennewitz, Trans.). New York: Viking Press, A Studio Book.

Singer, J. (1972). *Boundaries of the soul: The practice of Jung's psychology.* Garden City, NY: Doubleday.

Singer, J. (1990). *Seeing through the visible world: Jung, gnosis, and chaos.* San Francisco: Harper & Row.

Stettbacher, K. J. (1991). *Making sense of the suffering. The healing confrontation with your own past.* New York: Dutton.

Walker, B. G. (1988). *The woman's dictionary of symbols and sacred objects.* San Francisco: Harper & Row.

Whitmont, E. C. (1978). *The symbolic quest: Basic concepts of analytical psychology.* Princeton, NJ: Princeton University Press.

Whitmont, E. C., & Perera, S. B. (1989). *Dreams: A portal to the source.* London and New York: Routledge.

Zweig, C. (Ed.) (1990). *To be a woman: The birth of the conscious feminine.* Los Angeles: Jeremy P. Tarcher.

Zweig, C., & Abrams, J. (Eds.). (1991). *Meeting the shadow: The hidden power of the dark side of human nature.* Los Angeles: Jeremy P. Tarcher, Inc.

Final Note

D ick and I met a year after I moved to Central Washington. We have been married for 26 years. We share a commitment to following the path of art as the vitalizing force in our lives. Consequently, our home is a whimsical art site, "Dick and Jane's Spot." Although it is not open to the public, people enjoy driving or walking around it. So while I have been working on these difficult images in the studio, I have been buoyed by the sound of laughter coming through the open window. Whenever the seriousness of life has threatened to overwhelm us, Dick and I could go out in the yard and play together, creating something wacky and wonderful.